Access to Geography 2

Richard Kemp ● **Rebecca Mason** ● **Tim Sims**

Oxford University Press

Acknowledgements

The publishers and authors would like to thank the following people for their permission to use copyright material:

Aerofilms p34; APL/ZEFA p44; Bruno Barbey/Magnum Photos p74 (left); Bettmann/ Hulton Picture Co p60; John Birdsall Photography p68 (bottom); Warren Bolster/ Tony Stone Photolibrary-London p32; British Coal Opencast p52; British Railways Board pp 86 (top left), 87 (bottom); Simon Bruty/ Allsport p68 (top right); Carrard/Gamma/ Frank Spooner Pictures p68 (centre); The J Allan Cash Photolibrary p57; Cliff Christie p50; City of Bristol pp 18–19; Sue Cunningham pp 74 (right), 78 (top), 79 (centre); Richard Denyer/Broads Authority p48; Sally & Richard Greenhill p66 (bottom); Hutchinson Library p78 (bottom); Donald Innes Studios p83; InterCity p87 (top); D Jardine p62 (top centre, top right and bottom centre); Stephen Johnson/Tony Stone Photolibrary-London p22; Lovell Partnerships p16 (top); Tony Morrison/South American Pictures pp72, 79 (bottom); Novosti/Gamma/Frank Spooner Pictures p36; Gilles Peress/Magnum Photos p71; HRH The Prince of Wales p45; QA Photos pp 88, 90 (bottom); Rex Features p42; Carlos Reyes/Andes Press Agency pp 68 (top right), 75, 77, 78 (centre), 79 (top); F Salmoiraghi/ ZEFA p40; Sealand Aerial Photography p7; Southampton Container Terminals Ltd p80; Frank Spooner Pictures p69; Swadlincote Ski Centre p55 (top); Tesco Creative Services pp 23, 24; Tudor Photography p26; TV-am p68 (bottom left); Viewfinder Colour Photo Library p16 (bottom); John Walmsley pp 62 (top left, bottom left, bottom right) 66 (top, centre left, centre right) 86, 90 (top, centre) 93; Tony Waltham p47; ZEFA p20; Courtesy of National Park Authorities as shown p49.

Other photos have been provided by authors.

The cover photograph is reproduced by permission of Tony Stone Worldwide.

The Ordnance Survey map extracts on pages 14, 17, and 54 are reproduced with the permission of the Controller of Her Majesty's Stationery Office © Crown copyright.

Poem, p44: © Alan Bold 1987, reprinted from 'Another Fifth Poetry Book' compiled by John Foster (OUP 1981) by permission of Alan Bold. Extract, p45: © Thomas Firbank 1940, reprinted from 'I Bought A Mountain' (Harrap 1940).

Every effort has been made to trace and contact copyright holders, but this has not always been possible. We apologise for any infringement of copyright.
Oxford University Press, Walton Street, Oxford OX2 6DP

Oxford New York Toronto
Delhi Bombay Calcutta Madras Karachi
Kuala Lumpur Singapore Hong Kong Tokyo
Nairobi Dar es Salaam Cape Town
Melbourne Auckland Madrid

and associated companies in
Berlin Ibadan

Oxford is a trade mark of Oxford University Press

© Oxford University Press 1992
First published 1992
Reprinted 1992, 1993

ISBN 0 19 833453 2

Typeset by Pentacor PLC, High Wycombe, Bucks
Artwork by Hardlines Ltd, Charlbury, Oxon

Printed in Italy by
G. Canale & C. S.p.A. - Borgaro T.se - TURIN

Introduction

Access to Geography has been carefully planned and written to meet the needs of the National Curriculum at Key Stage 3. The themes, topics, and case studies used in the three-book course are drawn from the National Curriculum programmes of study and are designed to cover all the appropriate statements of attainment.

The course has been planned as a practical response to the National Curriculum. The books have also been organised to match as much as possible the good practice geography teachers have developed in recent years. Each book is divided into half a dozen units, each based around a familiar unifying theme. Within each unit the material is organised in double-page spreads, the most practical format for classroom use.

The course is designed for students across a broad range of ability. The lively page design, the high quality visuals, the carefully-written text, and the range of student activities mean that the material is extremely accessible. Each book provides study material for a complete school year.

Differentiation

The books are designed to reflect the levels within Key Stage 3. Within the books each double-page spread contains a range of activities which allow students to work at their own level.

Geographical enquiry

Each book contains a variety of 'assignments' on double-page spreads. These are designed to encourage students in the development of their enquiry skills.

Regional case studies

Integrated within all the books are regional case studies. These exemplify and extend the material developing human, physical, and environmental themes and issues. Where appropriate, regional case studies are built on from one book to another.

Access to Geography is a practical and straightforward response to the needs of the National Curriculum.

CONTENTS

Settlements

Shopping patterns

Investigating landscapes

Managing landscapes

People on the move

Transport

1 In the beginning

Figure 1 The beginnings of four settlements

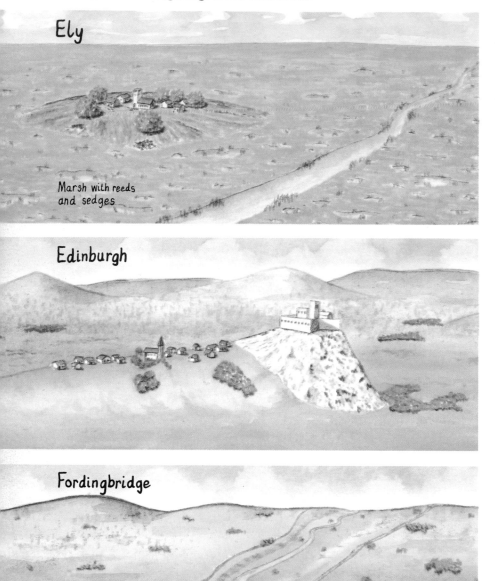

Ely

Marsh with reeds and sedges

Edinburgh

Fordingbridge

Corfe Castle

Have you ever thought about the name of the place where you live? Do you know what it means? Quite often the name of a place gives a clue about how the settlement began. All places have a beginning and the people who first chose to settle there had good reasons for doing so.

The four drawings on this page show the beginnings of four settlements. They were very different then, and they are still very different today. Each place had specific advantages, reasons that made it suitable for living in. These reasons, together with the land on which the place is built, make up the 'site' and 'situation' of a settlement.

> **Site**   The land on which a settlement is built.
> **Situation**   The land around the settlement.

Figure 2

Site and situation factors

1 **Protection, either from the landscape around or from invading neighbours!**

   Sites on hills, sites above land liable to flood, sites protected by natural features (e.g. inside river meanders).

2 **Transport and trade ('communications').**

   Settlements at crossroads, in between hills, at bridging and crossing points on rivers, ports.

3 **Mineral resources that could be exploited.**

   Settlements on clay, coal, or iron deposits (early industrial settlements would have been near woodland or water).

Origin of name	Place-name, or suffix, or prefix	English meaning
Celtic (from the Rhine and Danube Valleys)	axe, esk, usk, Ouse Avon Dee Dove Taw tre-, trev-, -cet -bre, -brig, -drum, pen-	water stream or river holy one black silent one homestead or village wood hill feature
Roman (from Italy)	-caster, -chester, -cester port	fort or castle harbour or gate
Saxon (from the valleys of Northern Germany)	-ing, -ingham -ham, -ington -ton -borough, -bury -stead -ley -stoke -rick -den -hurst, -hirst, -holt -rod, -riding -fen -mere -eg, -ey, -ea	groups of people homestead enclosure fortified place place clearing daughter settlement outlying hut or shelter pasture wooded area cleared land swamp lake island in a marsh
Scandinavian	-toft -by, -garth -booth -thorpe -thwaite -ey -dale -gill -ings -beck, -slack	homestead enclosure centre for summer pasture daughter settlement clearing island valley ravine marsh or meadow stream

Figure 3 The meanings of place-names

Figure 4 This aerial photograph shows how Warkworth is sited inside a river meander

Activities

1 Having read the text, try to explain the site and situation of the four settlements shown in Figure 1. Include in your answer a description of the land, the position of the settlement, and the reasons why it seems to be located there.

2 Figure 3 gives the meanings of many Anglo-Saxon place-name endings. The Saxons were responsible for founding many settlements throughout the country. Use your atlas to find examples of places with these endings and make a list of them.

3 Research idea:
Conduct some research into place-names in your area. Try to establish the history of settlement where you live. How long have people lived there? Does it still use its original site and situation advantages or have these disappeared? A local library or museum could hold the answers.

2 Growing and spreading

Figure 1 When put together, these jigmap pieces will make a simplified map of the growth of Derby

Key for jigmap

Period of growth

■	Up to 1791
■	1791 – 1880
□	1880 – 1914
■	Inter-war (1918 – 1939)
■	Post-war (since 1945)

——— Main roads

+++++ Railway

～～ River

■ Industry

For a long time the towns of this country remained small and clustered around their original site. Few people lived in towns, transport was difficult, and people depended on farming for their livelihood. Then came the Industrial Revolution and with it the move to towns for work. Towns started to grow outwards from their original site, but they remained fairly compact. Then the twentieth century arrived.

Advances in transport and better living standards encouraged the rapid growth and spread of our towns. By the beginning of the Second World War in 1939, most places covered an area twenty-five times larger than their area in 1800. The countryside was being taken over and was becoming part of the settlement. Most of the people were now urban rather than rural dwellers and depended on the town for their livelihood.

Derby has been an important settlement since Norman times. First a busy market town, then a manufacturing centre. England's very first silk mill was built there in 1717. In the nineteenth century the railway workshops brought massive expansion, to be followed in 1907 by Rolls Royce Ltd. Now over 200 000 people live and work in the city, and it is still growing and spreading.

Activities

1 Make careful copies of the jigmap pieces scattered around page 8. Include all the information inside the pieces as well as their outlines.

2 Cut out your jigmap pieces and try to fit them together. Glue your finished map together.

3 Use the scale bar in the key to work out Derby's growth in area. For each time period, measure the maximum width and maximum length of the city in kilometres. Now multiply your figures together. This will give you the area of the city. The first time period has been done for you.

Time period	Width (West-East) (km)	Length (North-South) (km)	Area (Km²)
Up to 1791	0.5	0.25	0.125

4 Draw a bar graph of your results with time on the horizontal axis and area in km² on the vertical axis.

5 What does the graph tell you about the growth of Derby? Is this obvious from the map? Write an account of the growth of Derby mentioning its beginnings, its fastest growth period, the directions of growth, and the areas by the river left unoccupied (why?).

6 Should settlements keep on spreading like this? Do we need to stop or control it? What do you think?

3 Assignment: On the agenda

Background information

As a settlement grows and develops, the needs of the residents and the area change. For a long time there were no rules governing who could build where, what, or when, and this led to haphazard expansion in towns and villages. Since the Second World War, however, laws have been passed by the government so that growth is controlled. This is the process called Town and Country Planning. Councils are responsible for producing a 'structure plan'. This gives details of how land is being used and what proposals there are for changes in the next few years. It explains what can and cannot be done in certain areas of the settlement so that order is kept in our neighbourhoods. So, if anyone is thinking of making changes or doing any building, they apply to the council for planning permission so that they can go ahead legally.

Figure 1 The council planning sub-committee

Environment
- Represents the environmental department of the council
- Responsible for keeping noise, waste, litter, and pollution to a minimum
- Happy with buildings that are attractive and blend in with their surroundings

The Chairperson
- Responsible for conducting the meeting
- Decides on the agenda of the meeting
- Makes sure everyone has a fair say
- Records the decisions
- As far as possible is neutral

Buildings / Surveyors
- Represents the technical department of the council
- Responsible for safety of buildings
- Has reservations about high-rise buildings
- Likes brick rather than concrete

Finance
- Represents the Treasury of the council
- Responsible for the allocation of council funds collected through the Community Charge
- Happy to see private schemes passed, but is reluctant to spend the council's funds

Parks & Leisure
- Responsible for both 'green area' opportunities and for recreation
- Happy with more open space and/or leisure opportunities for the people

Application No. 29369/B **From** Council Parks & Leisure Committee

For Purchase of warehouse and conversion into ten-pin bowling alley (municipal use).

Where Station Road

Specification The Parks & Leisure Committee see the potential of this one-storey brick-built warehouse as a recreation facility providing 20 bowling lanes with snack bar and associated car parking.

Comments Other application for the same site from 'D.I.Y.Interiors Ltd' for use as a superstore (No.29370/B).

Application No. 27641/B **From** Mr. H. Andrews

For Conversion of a greengrocers into a fish & chip shop.

Where Harbury Road, Davenport Estate

Specification The building is in the middle of an arcade of shops on this estate. A flue chimney from the fat fryers will be installed at the rear to a height of 4 metres.

Comments All alterations to be paid for by Mr. Andrews with a bank loan.

Application No. 28433/B **From** Winstanley Building Contractors

For Demolition of building owned by the council and erection of an office block.

Where High Street

Specification The council building is currently unused. Winstanley will undertake demolition and erection of a five-storey concrete and glass office block to be leased by them privately.

Comments Planning permission for demolition already granted (No.19938/B).

Figure 2 Planning applications

Your assignment

In this assignment you are going to take on the role of the council planning sub-committee who are meeting to discuss three of the latest applications. So, what is on the agenda? Working in groups of five, follow the procedure outlined in the Work Programme.

Work Programme

- Decide on your roles for the meeting (Figure 1).
- In your role, prepare for the meeting by studying the applications carefully (Figure 2). Decide what you think about each one. Have your ideas ready when the chairperson asks you.

- Now hold your meeting. The chairperson will explain how it is to be conducted. Consider each application in turn and decide whether to accept or reject it.
- Record the decisions of the committee and their reasons.
- Now meet together as a whole class and compare the decisions of the different committees.
  a) Were they all in agreement?
  b) How were the decisions taken by each group? Who had the final say? Why?

4 Patterns in the area

Think about your school for a minute! How is it organised? If you attend an average-sized secondary school then it is likely to have an organisation similar to that in Figure 1. The structure looks like a pyramid. Each layer is part of the whole, but does a specific job. Notice too that as you go 'up' the pyramid, there are fewer members and that they have a more specialised function. This sort of arrangement is called a hierarchy, and is also found in the pattern of settlement in an area.

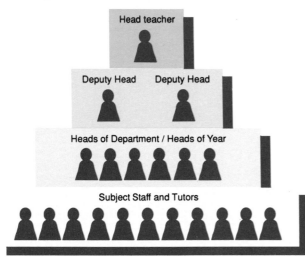

Figure 1 The school hierarchy

As settlements grow they may change their function and their character. In any one area some settlements will remain small whilst others will continue to grow and dominate the area. This will give us a hierarchy arrangement with the same rules as the school hierarchy. There will be many low-order settlements, like villages, which offer few services. Middle-order settlements, like towns, will be fewer, but will have rather more services. At the top of the hierarchy there is likely to be one high-order settlement, like a city, which will have many specialised services. This dominant settlement will serve the whole area, and people will use it for the functions it provides that they cannot find in their own middle- or low-order settlement. We describe this area as the 'service area', 'hinterland', or 'sphere of influence' of the settlement.

In low-order settlements, the population is too small to support a wide variety of services. The opposite is true of a high-order settlement. Consequently, the higher the order of the settlement, the larger the sphere of influence.

The map in Figure 3 shows some of the settlement hierarchy surrounding Cambridge in East Anglia. What is the pattern of settlement in any particular area? Are there any rules we can see which explain the pattern?

Figure 2 Threshold populations for certain shops and services

Shop or service	Number of people living in the settlement's sphere of influence needed to support shop or service	
General store	200	**Low threshold** shops and services found in all towns and cities and most large villages. These services are required by most people every week.
Primary school	250	
Butcher	350	
Newsagent	750	
Greengrocer	2 500	
Post Office	2 500	
Public House	3 500	
Doctor's surgery	3 500	
Branch library	12 000	**Middle threshold** shops and services found only in towns and cities.
Bank	15 000	
Secondary school	17 000	
Swimming pool	50 000	
Cinema	50 000	
Chain store (e.g.Boots)	50 000	
Museum	70 000	
Art gallery	200 000	**High threshold** shops and services found only in major towns and cities.
General hospital	200 000	
Concert hall	300 000	
Polytechnic/University	300 000	
Department store	350 000	

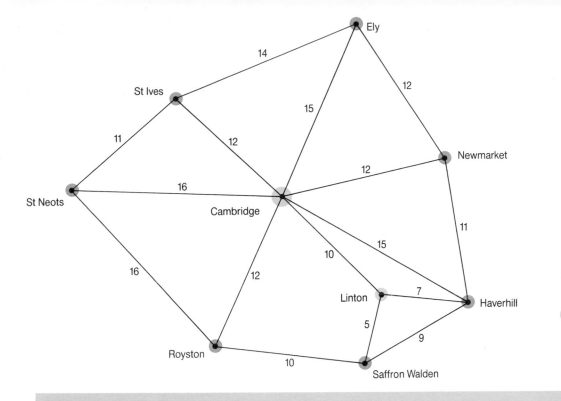

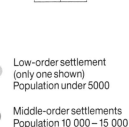

0   2   4 Miles

⬤ Low-order settlement
(only one shown)
Population under 5000

⬤ Middle-order settlements
Population 10 000 – 15 000

⬤ High-order settlement
Population over 100 000

12   Distance in miles between
settlements

Figure 3 The pattern
of settlements around
Cambridge

Activities

1 The table in Figure 2 gives the threshold population for different services. The threshold population is the minimum number of people needed in the sphere of influence for the service to be provided. Low-order settlements support low threshold services, and high-order settlements support high threshold services. Answer the following statements *true* or *false*.
a) There will be a post office in Linton.
b) St Neots will have a secondary school.
c) Only Cambridge will have a bank.
d) Saffron Walden will have a hospital.
e) There will be no primary schools in Ely.

2 If you were the following people, where would you go? Give a reason for your answer in each case.
a) An elderly resident of Linton who needs some groceries.
b) A family from Haverhill who are going to do the weekly shopping.
c) A couple from St Neots on an evening out.

3 There are rules which seem to govern hierarchies and the Cambridge hierarchy follows this pattern.
a) What is the rule about the distance between middle-order settlements?
b) What is the rule about the distance from a middle-order to a high-order settlement?
c) What is the rule about the population of a middle-order compared to a low-order settlement?
d) What is the rule about the population of a middle-order compared to a high-order settlement?

4 Research idea:
Produce a hierarchy map for settlements in your own area similar to the Cambridge map. Are the rules the same in your area? Can you explain any variations?

5 Patterns in the city: the model

The town centre

This is the heart of the town. It is likely to be the place from which the town began to grow. All the major buildings are in this area, and it is where commercial activities like shops and offices are found. The amount of space is usually limited, so buildings are often multi-storey. It is called the Central Business District or CBD because hardly anyone lives here anymore.

● On the map, look for large buildings, lots of road intersections, and special features like cathedrals or hospitals.

- Central Business District (CBD)
- Redevelopment zone
- Factory zone
- Terraced housing
- Suburban housing
- Commuter housing

The industrial area

Outside the town centre, often on the eastern side, is where the traditional industries are located. The land here was not as expensive as the town centre, but it was still close enough for good communications.

● On the map, look for railway lines and large units with space around them. Sometimes there will be particular labels like 'Mill' or 'Wks' or even 'Factory'. In certain cities or towns, the riverside is often associated with this zone.

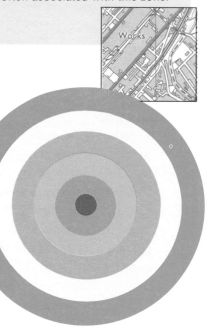

Figure 1 A model showing land use in towns, with a description of each zone. The map extracts were taken from an Ordnance Survey 1:25 000 map

Area of redevelopment

Mixed in between the CBD and the industrial area is an area of change. Where old industries have closed down or housing has become unfit for living, redevelopment takes place. This area is close to the CBD and so is very attractive to developers for office complexes, light modern industries, or, more usually, high-class housing.

● On the map, this is the most difficult area to identify as there are very few clues. We need more help than the map can give to see this area clearly.

Area of terraced housing

Right next to the industrial area is where the workers lived. During the Industrial Revolution, factory owners built houses for their staff in long terraced rows. Their efficient use of space made terraces popular again during the inter-war years (1918-39).

● On the map, look for the 'gridiron' pattern showing long rows of houses and square road patterns.

Commuter housing

As car ownership became widespread, many people looked for a home outside the town. The surrounding villages were chosen as long as the journey to town was still possible along easy routes.

● On the map, look for areas that have separate names, even though they may now be hardly separate from the town.

Suburban housing

As the town grew, the workers moved out to new houses further away from their workplace. They were able to do this because of improvements in transport. They wanted to have more living space, so they chose housing estates with gardens. Eventually, these houses showed a pattern of their own, with 'plots' of semi-detached houses with garages and gardens.

● On the map, look for curving road patterns on estates, with housing blocks hugging the roads.

What sort of house do you live in? Is it the same as your neighbour's? Are all the houses in the street like this? What about other people in the class? It depends on what area of the town you live in. Different areas in the towns and cities in which we live have different characters. And each area seems to have a certain function, a reason for being there. In trying to provide an explanation of why there are areas or 'zones' in our settlements, geographers have developed a model of land use for towns. It is illustrated in Figure 1.

There are two ideas that are important to understanding the model:

1 The nearer the city centre, the more expensive the land. The competition for space is fierce, and only those who can afford the high land prices will be located here.
2 All settlements develop outwards from a core. The further away from the city centre a place is, the more recent its development.

A model is a simple but useful way of looking at things. It can give us a starting point for understanding patterns. It also gives us a way of comparing how well things match up to the ideas in the model. But be careful with models. Not everything in the model will be seen in every place. Do not try and make things 'fit' that do not, instead try and explain why things are exceptions. You have a chance to do this in the next section. Remember too that land use in towns is always changing and so zones may appear or disappear or change their location or size. Maps or photographs are static, but the places in which we live and work are dynamic, a kaleidoscope of changing patterns.

Activities

1 Visit your local estate agents and ask for property leaflets about houses for sale in different parts of the town. (The local newspaper is also useful for this.)
2 Now plot your findings onto a base map of the town. For each property put a '●', number it, and write down when it was built (if known) and its price, like this:

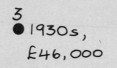

3 Decide where the town centre is and mark it on the map. Measure the distance from here to each property and record the results in a table, like this:

Number	Distance from town centre (km)	Age (years)	Price (£000s)
1	3	5	70

4 Plot your findings on two graphs. Scatter the points as shown below.

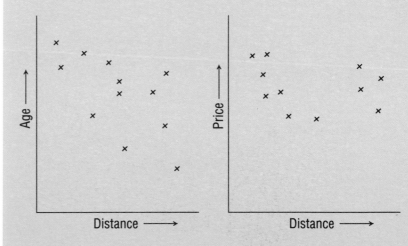

5 What do your graphs show? Are the oldest houses nearer to the centre? Are the most expensive houses nearer to the centre? Write a paragraph about your findings.

6 Patterns in the city: Bristol

The model in the last section showing how functional zones develop in a town was first applied to cities in the USA. Since then it has been shown to be a useful way of looking at a number of cities and towns right across the developed world.

Bristol is one of the ten biggest cities in the United Kingdom. But has Bristol got the same zones and patterns?

Figure 1 (right) An area of redevelopment in Bristol. This attractive residential environment was previously an area of old and derelict warehouses

Figure 2 The Floating Harbour, Bristol

Activities

1 Place a large sheet of tracing paper over the Ordnance Survey (OS) map extract. Now try to pick out the areas and boundaries of the different zones. Look for:
a) the Central Business District (CBD);
b) areas of redevelopment just outside the CBD;
c) industrial areas;
d) areas of terraced housing;
e) housing estates in the inner suburbs;
f) the outer suburbs.
Shade in these areas on your map and use a colour key to identify them.

2 Now compare your map with the model in the last section. In what ways are they similar and different?

3 Write an explanation of 'The pattern of land use in Bristol', paying special interest to the reasons why the areas are where they are.

Figure 3 Bristol, from an Ordnance Survey 1:50 000 map

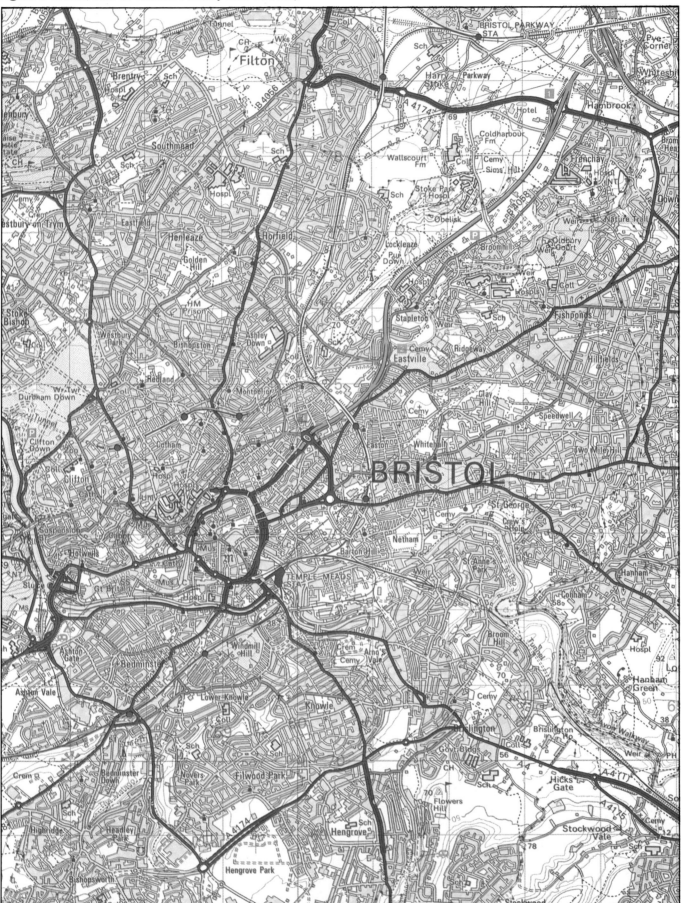

7 Assignment: A new heart for Bristol

Figure 1
Bristol city centre

Figure 2 The Planning Department's ideas for the city centre

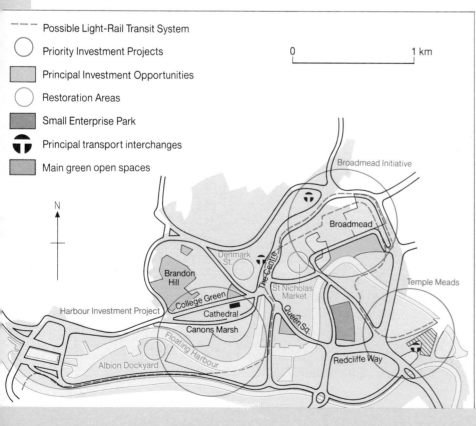

- - - Possible Light-Rail Transit System
○ Priority Investment Projects
▢ Principal Investment Opportunities
○ Restoration Areas
▮ Small Enterprise Park
🛈 Principal transport interchanges
▮ Main green open spaces

0   1 km

Background information

In the eighteenth century, Bristol was one of the country's main ports. But the size of ships increased and Bristol's harbour facilities became unsuitable. The port declined and today a large area near the city centre is ripe for redevelopment.

Your assignment

Work in small groups for this assignment. The Bristol City Planning Department has come up with a draft structure plan which explains how the city centre is going to be redeveloped. There are three major areas under consideration and the details of each are shown in Figures 2 and 3.

Your group has been given the job of advertising these projects. How you must do this is set out in the Work Programme.

Figure 3 The Priority Investment Projects

TEMPLE MEADS

The Plan sees the development of the area mainly for commercial purposes but does not envisage a monopoly of office uses. Other commercial uses might include conference facilities and trade centre, a 'one-stop' business service centre, an hotel and some shopping for visitors and travellers. The Bristol Exploratory, a 'hands-on' science and technology exhibition, is already established in Brunel's old station building. A vital element of development here will be a major transport interchange bringing together the railway, any light-rail transit proposal, buses, taxis, and the ferry service. The harbour walkway network will also link the area with other parts of the City Centre.

BROADMEAD INITIATIVE

The city's main shopping centre will continue the process of transformation which has begun with the construction of 'The Galleries' - an indoor shopping mall on three levels. Already there are proposals for further major developments extending the centre to the north and east. All of this will provide the necessary stimulus for the other improvements to the shopping environment and future upgrading of the unattractive parts of Broadmead. In conjunction with this, Castle Park, which links the shopping centre with the Floating Harbour, is to be completely remodelled to provide an open-air arena, children's play area, informal gardens and walks with scope for waterside activities and a ferry point.

HARBOUR INVESTMENT PROJECT

Canon's Marsh/Wapping Wharf is possibly the most prestigious and exciting development opportunity in the region. It is being studied by development consultants working for a consortium of landowners including the City Council. Amongst the City Council's objectives are the provision of a new performance hall, a leisure and entertainment complex, a swimming pool, expansion of the Maritime Heritage Centre and Museums and the creation of a network of attractive and convenient pedestrian routes linking urban spaces of high quality. Other development opportunities include housing, hotel and conference facilities, exhibition space and speciality shopping. These higher value land uses will help secure the necessary funding for the less-profitable elements.

Work Programme

- For each of the Priority Investment Project (PIP) areas detailed in Figure 3, produce a number of plans and/or sketches to give an impression of what it might look like after redevelopment. It may be better to concentrate on certain buildings in each PIP rather than drawing the whole thing.
- For each of the PIP areas, produce a fact sheet that can be given to local businesses who might enquire about the possibilities in each area. The fact sheet needs to explain the Planning Department's ideas in an enthusiastic way so that money will be provided for the plans. (If you have access to a word processor, you could use it to make your finished product look good.)
- The city planners have to address a public meeting about the projects. Produce a script that they might use on this occasion. You could tape it yourselves or even video it.
- Finally, your work is going to become part of a public exhibition. Produce your work on a wall display in the classroom.

1 Spoilt for choice

Figure 1 Marlborough High Street – a typical small-town High Street. This photo also shows market day, another shopping choice

'Won't be long. Just nipping out for a loaf of bread and some milk.'

A familiar comment in many homes, but where would you go? Have you got a choice? For all of us the answer is 'yes'. Items like bread and milk could be purchased in a number of different types of shop, from the local 'corner shop' to the supermarket and other shops in between. The choice we make will affect the shops in different ways. For some it will be the difference between remaining open or closing down. For others it will add to their profits and keep them growing. The way in which we shop can be studied in geography because of the patterns it makes. These patterns can be in space (where we shop) or in time (how often we shop). Shopping patterns have changed a great deal in the last twenty years, and they are continuing to change. As a result, the type, number, and location of our shops has changed too. The Figures in this section and the text and Figures in the next section will help us understand the pattern of change and the impact of the choices we have made about how we shop.

Figure 2 The local shops

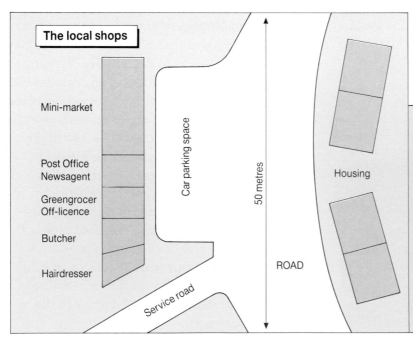

Figure 2 The local shops

A row or 'parade' or shops, in this case on a housing estate two miles from the town centre. The shops are on a road running through the estate. Built about thirty years ago at the same time as the houses, the shops are fronted by car parking space. They are open six days a week and are very busy at the beginning and end of the working day serving the households on the estate. Some, like the mini-market, stay open late (8p.m.) so that they can serve people coming home from work.
Most customers are regulars who make it a habit to 'pop in', often to more than one of the shops.

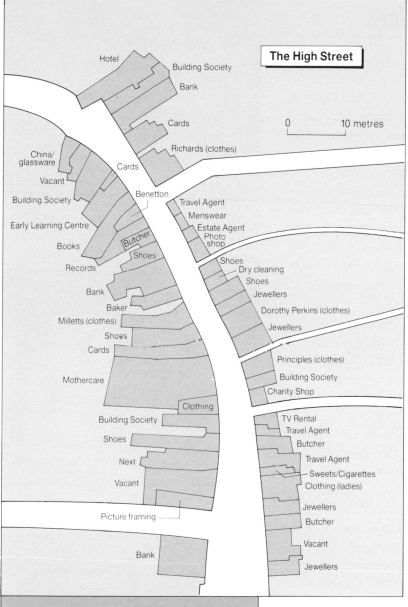

The High Street

Hotel
Building Society
Bank
Cards

0   10 metres

Richards (clothes)
China/glassware
Cards
Vacant
Benetton
Building Society
Travel Agent
Early Learning Centre
Menswear
Estate Agent
Books
Butcher
Photo shop
Shoes
Shoes
Records
Shoes
Dry cleaning
Bank
Shoes
Baker
Jewellers
Milletts (clothes)
Dorothy Perkins (clothes)
Shoes
Jewellers
Cards
Mothercare
Principles (clothes)
Building Society
Clothing
Charity Shop
Building Society
TV Rental
Shoes
Travel Agent
Butcher
Next
Travel Agent
Vacant
Sweets/Cigarettes
Clothing (ladies)
Picture framing
Jewellers
Butcher
Bank
Vacant
Jewellers

A wide variety of shops on either side of the High Street in the town centre. In this case, the road is part of the town's one-way system and there is no daytime parking. The shops vary in size. They open six days a week, although some have an 'early-closing' day on Wednesdays. The customers come from all parts of the town and the surrounding villages. They have usually made a definite decision to shop here, either for specific goods or a specialist service they cannot get elsewhere. The 'mix' of shops in the High Street changes as custom varies. Only thirty out of the fifty shops have been here for more than five years.

Figure 3 The High Street

Activities

1 Here is a shopping list for a family living on the housing estate close to the local shops. Decide which items can be bought locally and which they need to go to the town centre for. Give reasons for your decision.

> Film for camera / have film developed.
>
> ½ dozen brown rolls
> 1 lb tomatoes
> Magazine
> Joint for Sunday
> Julie's birthday card/present
> Breakfast cereals

2 Make a tracing of the layout of the High Street. Now group the shops in the following categories and colour in your map:

- Food shops
- Clothes shops
- Other products
- Shops selling services

3 From your map, try to describe the function that the High Street now plays in our shopping choice.

4 Choose three of the High Street shops and for each say what the advantages and disadvantages are of its present position in the street.

5 Make a list of the businesses you expect will still be in the High Street in five years time. Why do you think so?

2 Changing choices

Few people still live in town centres. The Central Business District (CBD) is a place for work and leisure, not housing. Towns have grown outwards as more people with cars commute to work and live out of the centre. This growth has also had a big effect on shopping. Did you know that one of the most important selling points of a car is what you can get in it – be it a suitcase, DIY wardrobe, or grand piano! There is an important link between cars and shopping habits.

Another change is that many more families are now out working during the day. Fewer people shop during the day on a weekday. After work and at weekends are now the most popular shopping times.

How have shopping patterns reflected our changing habits? One response was to build shopping malls or centres. These are indoor or covered areas containing large shops and chain stores, and they are designed to make shopping an easy and pleasant pastime – 'all under one roof', as the advertising goes. Figures 1 and 2 show two different shopping centres.

Figure 1 A modern multi-level indoor shopping centre: The Pavilions, Birmingham

Figure 2 A plan of Central Milton Keynes Shopping Centre at the heart of Milton Keynes New City

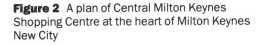

Legend:
- Department stores/Supermarkets
- Electrical goods
- Clothes/Shoes
- Food shops/Restaurants/Pubs
- Specialist shops
- Services (Banks, Estate Agents, etc.)
- Public Services (Post Office, Job Centre)

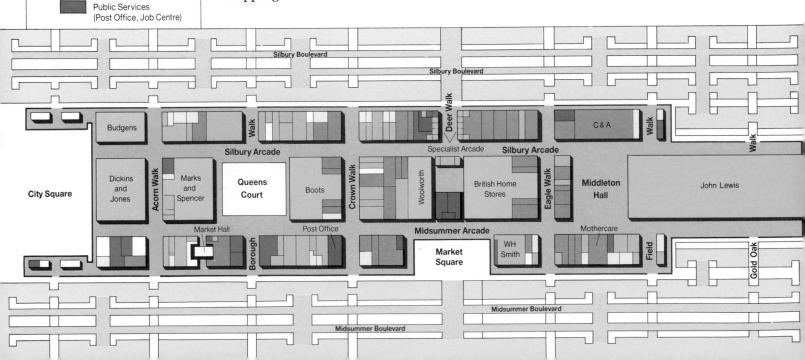

Figure 3 The out-of-town superstore: Tesco, Rugby

A second and more recent idea is the out-of-town superstore. Figure 3 shows the Tesco site in Rugby. Superstores sell a wide range of food and household goods. They have large car parks and are close to main roads as they are used by people with cars. Linked to the store is often a cut-price petrol station as an added attraction. At the moment, developments like this are still taking place all over the country. But, as we move into the twenty-first century, the pattern of shopping will continue to change.

Activities

1 The car has changed our shopping habits. For each of the following say what changes the car has brought about and give reasons for these changes.
   a) The amount of shopping purchased.
   b) The number of visits to the shops each week.
   c) The facilities required for shopping.

2 Put the following list of factors into two columns to show the differences between town centre and out-of-town shopping.

   Cheaper land prices
   Easier access by car
   Wider choice of goods
   Easier car parking
   Specialist services available
   More frequent bus service
   Major chain stores are there
   Bulk buying is cheaper
   Late night opening available

3 Imagine you are the manager of a supermarket in the town centre. Describe your reactions to the opening of a new out-of-town superstore by a competitor in a letter to the local newspaper.

3 Tesco's choice

When did you last visit a supermarket? Probably very recently. Nearly all of us choose to shop in this way, saying it is 'convenient'. And for a growing number of us supermarket convenience no longer means having to go in to town – the out-of-town superstore is where we do our weekly shop.

Over the last ten years in particular, as the graph in Figure 4 shows, the large supermarket retailers have been choosing out-of-town sites for their superstores. You would have to live somewhere quite remote not to have one in your area. Just look at the map in Figure 1 – and that is only new Tesco superstores in two years. Imagine the pattern if we added ASDA, Sainsbury, Waitrose, Gateway, and the rest!

Not only are the sites for these stores similar, but the style of shopping and facilities on offer all follow a prescribed pattern. Our habits are so predictable that the marketing department of the superstore can tell the store manager what sales can be expected for any item, for any week, for any location in the country, and then confidently expects that to be the store's target. So the next time you are queuing up at the till, imagine the millions of others who are doing the same. Do we really have a choice?

Figure 1 New Tesco superstores in England and Wales, 1988–1990

Figure 2 The Tesco superstore at Stroud

What the supermarkets offer		
Facility	Sainsbury	Tesco
Average number of checkouts	26	26
	Percentage of stores	
Car parks	94	86
Late opening	100	100
Early opening	95	100
Public toilets	35	33
Cafe/Snack Bar	12	26
Baby changing room	20	15
In-store bakery	65	56
Fresh fish counter	20	46
Delicatessen	65	82
Free carrier bags	100	100
Express checkout	100	95
Credit card payment	0	100
EFTPOS* payment	95	31

*Electronic Funds Transfer at Point of Sale

Figure 3

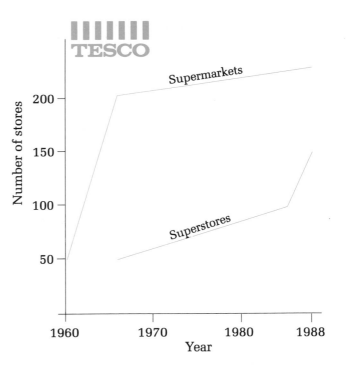

Figure 4 The growth of Tesco, 1960–1988

Activities

1 Look at the map in Figure 1 showing the growth of Tesco stores in the period 1988–1990. Write a paragraph to describe this pattern. Use the following questions to help you structure your answer.

a) Are the stores clustered (all together) or dispersed (spread out)?

b) What part of the country has the most stores?

c) How is this distribution related to where the people live? (Use an atlas map of population to help you.)

2 Look at the graph in Figure 4 showing the growth of supermarkets and superstores in the period 1960–1988.

a) How many supermarkets were open in 1960?

b) In what decade did most supermarkets open?

c) How many superstores were there in 1988?

d) What changing pattern of growth does this show?

3 The table in Figure 3 compares the facilities of Tesco and Sainsbury supermarkets. What are the main similarities and differences between them? Answer using the following table.

Similarities	Differences
Difference of 5% or less	Difference of 10% or more

4 Conduct a class survey of shopping habits. Do most people use supermarkets? If so, which ones? What facilities offered by the different supermarkets influence their choice?

5 Draw some graphs to show the results of your survey. Now explain the shopping choices of your class. Do they match the changes suggested in these sections? Are more people using out-of-town facilities these days?

4 Trader's choice: the retail park

Figure 1 Three views of Banbury Cross Retail Park

This was taken from an advertising billboard:

FOR SALE

Disused factory and accompanying buildings on main road out of town

Offers in the region of
£1.25 million

Figure 2

If you had had the money, what would you have done? In this case the answer was quite dramatic. The developers knocked down all the factory buildings, landscaped the area, and then submitted plans for a retail park. But what is a retail park? Figure 1 shows the finished product. You could look on it as the 'trader's choice'. They are suggesting new ways for us to shop. We have seen how shopping patterns have changed because of the car and working practice. The retail park takes the change one stage further.

Certain types of shops can take advantage of large out-of-town premises and set up 'warehouse shopping'. This is what a retail park is really all about. Providing the site has good road access and plenty of car parking space, any out-of-town location can work. Add to that the facts that the occupiers will be household names through television advertising, that they will stay open late at night and over the weekend, and that they will offer discount prices, and you have a recipe for shopping success in the 1990s.

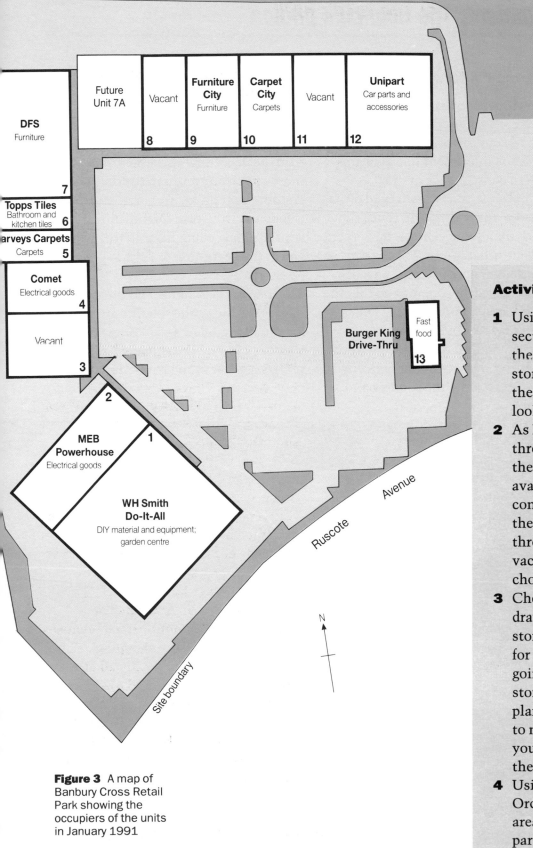

Figure 3 A map of Banbury Cross Retail Park showing the occupiers of the units in January 1991

Activities

1 Using all the information in this section, list what you think are the common features of all the stores on the retail park. What are the things that they are all looking for in this location?

2 As Figure 3 shows, in January 1991, three months after the park opened, there were three vacant units available. Decide on the type of companies that will be interested in these units and then allocate your three most likely companies to the vacant plots. Give reasons for the choices you make.

3 Choose any two of the units and draw an outline plan, to scale, of the store. (A piece of graph paper is best for this.) Now decide how you are going to organise the inside of the store. Draw your ideas onto your plan. How have you fitted things in to make it easy for shoppers? Have you made the most use of space in the store for selling?

4 Using a 1:50 000 or 1:25 000 Ordnance Survey map of your local area, select a suitable site for a retail park. Now draw a sketch map with labels showing the advantages of this site as a development.

5 Assignment: The council's choice

Background information

The previous sections have explained some of the changes in shopping patterns in our towns, the biggest of which is the movement to out-of-town sites. As a consequence of this locational shift, many towns and cities have had to think carefully about the future of their town centres. If everyone moves out, what is left? The answer, of course, is to make the town centre an attractive place for shopping so that the trend is halted if not reversed. This means a new sort of town centre.

Many councils have decided that the best way to improve the shopping in towns is to separate the shopper and their transport. The result of this is often a pedestrianised area in the town. Here, vehicles are strictly limited. As road space becomes pavement, there are more opportunities to make the general environment pleasant.

Banbury, in North Oxfordshire, has seen the local council act in this way, and at the beginning of 1991 a pedestrianisation scheme was started. The map of the scheme and the press release outlining the scheme are printed for you in Figures 1 and 2. But is it wanted? How do the shoppers and the traders feel about the council's choice?

Figure 1 The pedestrianisation scheme for Banbury town centre

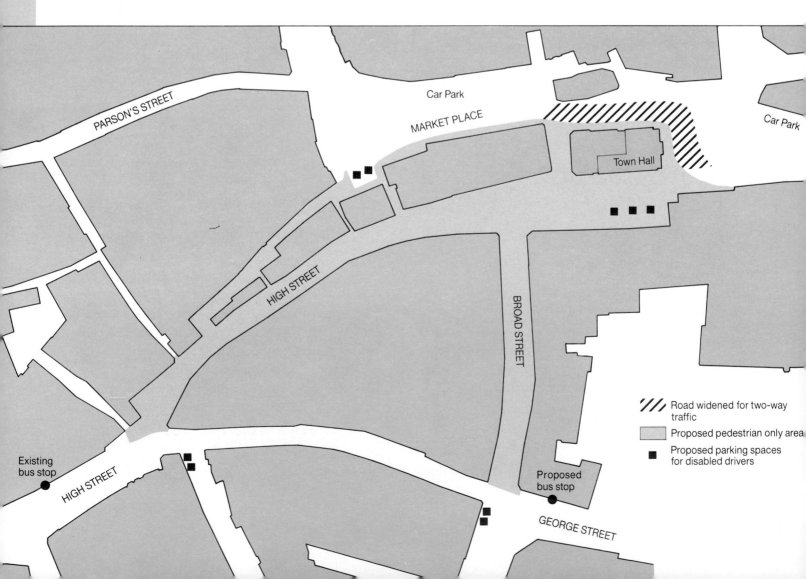

Road widened for two-way traffic

Proposed pedestrian only area

Proposed parking spaces for disabled drivers

Your assignment

Although the scheme has the go-ahead, the council are anxious to gauge reaction. You have been given the job of providing the means by which this is to be done. The details of what you must do are set out in the Work Programme.

Figure 2 The council's press release

DISTRICT COUNCIL PRESS RELEASE

BANBURY TOWN CENTRE PEDESTRIANISATION SCHEME

Banbury's long-awaited pedestrianisation scheme is expected to take eight months to complete. The scheme involves extensive environmental improvements to town centre streets coupled with new road-traffic and car-parking orders which will exclude traffic from these streets during the main part of the day.

The appearance of these streets will be completely altered and improved by:
* the laying of new concrete blocks and clay paving, and the elimination of kerbstones
* the introduction of new street furniture - seats, litter bins, lighting - new street signs, tree planting and floral displays;
* the construction of a special focal feature at the junction of High Street, Bridge Street, and Broad Street.

Between 10.30a.m. and 4.00p.m., shoppers and other persons on foot will have exclusive use of these streets, and all motor traffic will be excluded during this period (save for bullion and emergency vehicles, disabled-drivers permit holders, and buses outward-bound along Bridge Street and down Broad Street until the inner relief road is open). Outside these times access will be allowed for essential service vehicles into the streets.

New parking for disabled motorists will be provided.

The council believes that
* the town centre will become a more attractive and a safer place in which to shop and move around;
* more shoppers will be attracted into the centre, into a pleasant traffic-free environment without congestion and conflict from motor vehicles;
* the scheme will be of benefit to both shoppers and traders alike.

Whilst it is inevitable that a certain degree of disruption to the public and traders will occur during the construction period, the Council will do everything possible to keep this to a minimum.

Chief Planning Officer
21st December 1990

Work Programme A

- You need to design and test two questionnaires that could be used to gauge public opinion. The two sample groups are (a) shoppers and (b) retailers. Think very carefully about the questions you will ask. The ideas set out in the press release in Figure 2 should help you.
- Now explain how your surveys are going to be carried out. Your report must answer at least the following:
  a) Who? – how will you choose your samples?
  b) How? – what way of asking will you use? – will they fill in a form or will you record their answers for them?
  c) Where? – where will the sample be collected? – how many sample points do you expect to need?
  d) When? – what time(s) and/or date(s)?
- Test out your questionnaires using members of your class, friends, and family as imaginary residents of Banbury. Which questions were successful? Why do you think so? Are there any that need changing in the light of your testing?

Work Programme B

- Fieldwork idea:
  a) If your local town has got a pedestrianised area, design a questionnaire to find out what people think of it. Has it been successful? Do shoppers and traders prefer it?
  b) If your local town does not have a pedestrianised area, design a questionnaire to see whether people would be in favour of one or not. You may like to send your results to the local council for consideration.

1 Assignment: Investigating churchyards

Background information

Have you ever been in a churchyard or cemetery and found yourself thinking for a moment about time passing by? As you stood there thinking, time went by. And all around you, there would have been evidence of the passage of time. How do things stand up to the passage of time? We all expect the rocks around us to last for ages, but even rocks change over time. Rocks change over time through a process called weathering. There are two main types of weathering activity. They are called chemical and mechanical weathering. Chemical weathering is where water and air produce chemical reactions in the rocks, so wearing them away. Mechanical weathering is where rocks are broken down along lines of weakness, like cracks, by extremes of temperature. Weathering depends on three things: rock type; climate; and time.

Your assignment

You are going to conduct a survey of a churchyard or cemetery in your area to look at the effects of weathering on gravestones. You need to collect information carefully and accurately. Your study should aim to answer two main questions:

1 What is the effect of age on the amount of weathering?
2 Are some rocks more easily weathered than others?

How you should do this is detailed in the Work Programme. Before going to the churchyard or cemetery, remember to ask permission from the vicar, priest, or local council.

GRAVEYARD VISIT RECORD SHEET

RECORD NUMBER ☐

1	Type of grave	Flat	☐
		Headstone	☐
		Tomb	☐
		Head & foot	☐
		Other	☐

2	Rock type	Marble	☐
		Limestone	☐
		Other	☐

| 3 | Date of first burial | ☐ ☐ ☐ |

4	Condition of stone	1 Sound	☐
		2 Leaning	☐
		3 Partly broken	☐
		4 Collapsed	☐
		5 Destroyed	☐

5	Condition of inscription (writing)	1 Perfect	☐
		2 Clear but worn	☐
		3 Most of it readable	☐
		4 Traces only, very little readable	☐
		5 Worn away	☐

Figure 1 (above)

Record Number	1 Type of grave					2 Rock type			3 Date of first burial	4 Condition of stone					5 Inscription				
	F	H	T	H/F	O	M	L	O		1	2	3	4	5	1	2	3	4	5
1		✓				✓			03 09 1962	✓					✓				
2			✓			✓			23 12 1949	✓						✓			

Figure 2 Table for summary of results

Work Programme

- Visit your local churchyard or cemetery and fill in your gravestone record form (Figure 1). You may want to collect a number of records yourself or work as a small or class group. You should aim to have fifty records completed as this represents a reasonable sample to work from.
- Now you need to bring all the information together. You may wish to use a table like that in Figure 2, but if your school has a database programme on computer that is available, put your records onto that.
- In order to see your results more clearly and so that you can answer the questions in the aims of this assignment, you can display your findings on two graphs.

Graph 1 is a scattergraph.
Age (column 3) is on the horizontal axis; weathering (column 5) is on the vertical axis. Plot each gravestone as a point (cross).

Graph 2 is a divided bar graph.
Weathering (column 5) is on the horizontal axis; number of gravestones in each category is on the vertical axis. Now subdivide each bar according to rock type (column 2), and colour it in.

- Now look carefully at your two graphs and answer the following questions:

Graph 1:
a) Are older gravestones more weathered? If so, your graph will look like this:

b) Is your pattern clear or are there exceptions? What are they? Why might this be so?

Graph 2:
a) Is one rock type more easily weathered? If so, your graph will look like this:

b) Is the pattern clear or are there exceptions? What are they? Why might this be so?

- Can you now answer the two questions in your aims? Put together a concluding paragraph to your study.

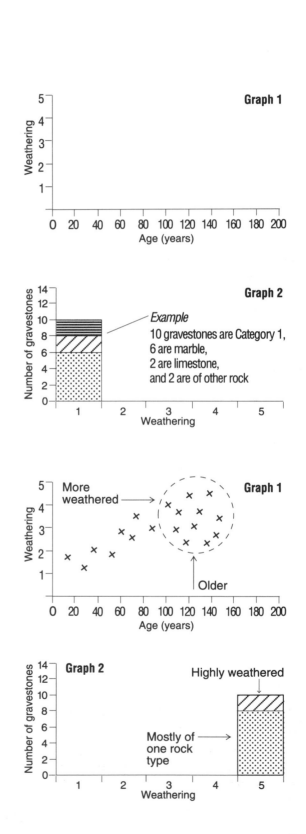

Graph 2
Example
10 gravestones are Category 1,
6 are marble,
2 are limestone,
and 2 are of other rock

2 The action of the sea

Figure 1 A spectacular close-up of a crashing wave

Figure 2 How constructive and destructive waves work

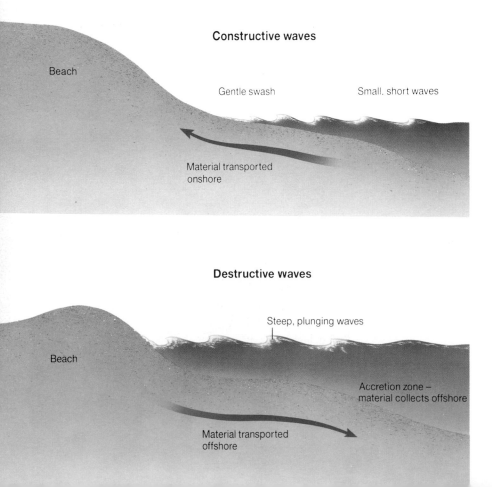

Constructive waves

Beach

Gentle swash

Small, short waves

Material transported onshore

Destructive waves

Steep, plunging waves

Beach

Accretion zone – material collects offshore

Material transported offshore

The fact that we live on an island has always made the sea very important to us. And over the last one hundred years seaside holidays have become very popular. If we were to investigate what the fascination is with the coast, most people would say the sea. From the person paddling at the shoreline to the surfer riding the waves, everyone enjoys and respects the action of the sea. But where do the waves come from and what effects do they have?

Waves are caused by the action of the wind on the surface of the water. The stronger the wind, the bigger and more powerful the waves that are formed. Large waves also occur when the wind has blown for a long distance over the sea. The length of water over which the wind has blown is known as the 'fetch'. The length of the fetch will depend on the distance to the nearest coastline.

When a wave breaks on the shoreline it has two motions, the forward motion or swash, and the backward motion or backwash. If the swash is more powerful than the backwash the wave is going to carry material up the beach. This is called a constructive wave. If, on the other hand, the backwash is the more powerful motion, the wave is going to carry material off the beach. This makes it a destructive wave. These two wave types are illustrated in Figure 2.

Where constructive waves are in operation, material will build up on the beach by the process of longshore drift (Figure 3). Often the material will collect on a headland, creating a long narrow ridge called a spit (Figure 4).

Where destructive waves operate, the coastline changes dramatically, producing many features. This is the subject of the next section.

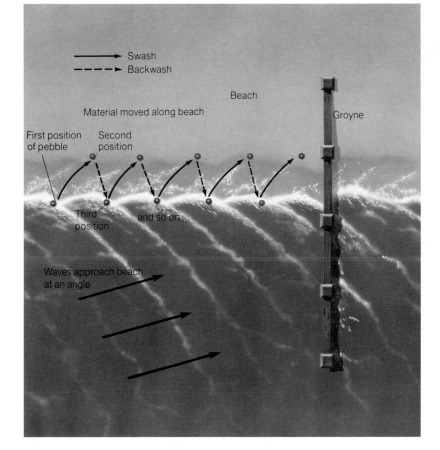

Figure 3 How the process of longshore drift works. Pebbles or sand are moved along a beach

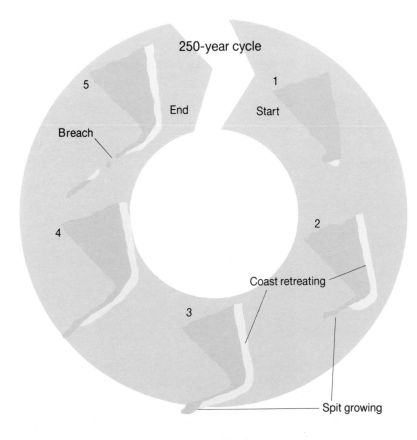

Figure 4 How a spit might grow over a period of 250 years

Activities

1 In your own words, explain the meaning of these terms. Draw diagrams to help your explanations.
   a) Swash
   b) Backwash
   c) Fetch

2 What causes a wave to be either constructive or destructive?

3 a) Using an atlas, draw an outline map of the British Isles and mark on arrows showing waves coming from the north-west, north-east, south-west, and south-east.
   b) Using an atlas again, measure the fetch (the distance travelled) of the waves coming from each of these four directions.
   c) Which coastlines in Britain are likely to be affected by the largest waves? Why?

4 Research idea:
   Figure 3 shows a groyne. Find out what it is put there for. What will happen as time passes? Is this a problem?

5 Research idea:
   Using maps and textbooks, investigate the following famous coastal spits:
   a) Spurn Head
   b) Chesil Beach
   c) Orford Ness
   For each one, find out where it is, where the material comes from, the wave direction, and any human interference or uses.

3 Coastal erosion

Cliff-peril house to be pulled down

Family lose home in cliff fall

Let cliffs crumble Nature Conservancy demand

EROSION THREAT TO SEA DEFENCE WORK

Figure 1 Newspaper headlines about coastal erosion

As well as the constructive, building action of the sea, waves have the power to change the scenery at the coast by erosion. There are four important ways that waves can erode:

1 Hydraulic action – the force of the waves themselves;
2 Corrasion – material carried by the sea is used to erode;
3 Attrition – material wears away by rubbing against itself;
4 Chemical action – salt water can react with certain rock types.

Each of these actions plays a part in eroding a cliffline to form a number of coastal features. Some of these are shown in Figure 2. The process of cliff erosion begins with wave attack undercutting the cliff at its base. This might produce a cave. Where there are two caves on opposite sides of a headland, they may join to form an arch. Eventually the arch roof may collapse, leaving a stack.

Although scenery like this is attractive to look at, the erosion of coasts can also cause danger. This is reflected in the newspaper headlines in Figure 1. Over the last thirty years, more and more coastal protection schemes have been put into operation. These vary in their complexity and cost. The simplest way of protecting cliffs is with a beach. Figure 3 shows a number of other schemes, all becoming more complex and expensive to install and maintain.

The decision about what can and should be done is a difficult one. Local authorities have to balance the cost of the scheme against the protection it gives, remembering that no scheme is 100 per cent effective at protecting people, property, or the coastline from the great and unpredictable power of the sea.

Figure 2 A chalk headland eroded by the sea: Handfast Point, Dorset

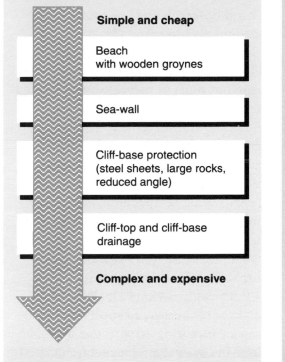

COASTAL PROTECTION SCHEMES

Simple and cheap

Beach with wooden groynes

Sea-wall

Cliff-base protection (steel sheets, large rocks, reduced angle)

Cliff-top and cliff-base drainage

Complex and expensive

Figure 3

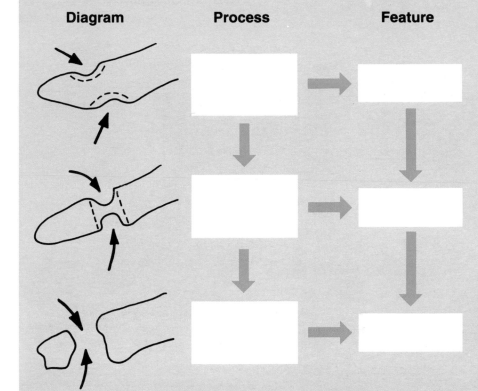

Diagram   Process   Feature

Figure 4 A flow diagram showing how a cliffline can be eroded. For use with Activity 1

Activities

1 Copy and complete Figure 4. Use the following information to fill in the spaces:

Destructive waves erode weakness in cliffline
Stack
Where caves are formed on both sides of headland they may join
Caves
Arch
The arch roof collapses

2 Now study the photograph of the Dorset coast (Figure 2). Draw a simple sketch of the photograph and label the following features:

Chalk cliffs   Cave   Stacks   Arch

3 Imagine that your class is the council of a seaside resort considering improving the coastal defences. At present there is a shingle beach with groynes backed by easily-eroded cliffs. The beach is 3km long. Full defences, as described in Figure 3, cost £1 million per kilometre to install. What action will your council take? How much are they prepared to spend? Consider your views (you may wish to take on a role such as a local hotel owner, a conservationist, or the Council Treasurer) and then organise a debate.

4 Earthquakes!

Figure 1 The aftermath of the Armenian earthquake, 1988

Suddenly there was a tremendous roar, as though a lot of railway trains were rattling and rumbling through the darkness of the room. A fine cloud of plaster began to fall from the ceiling. The outside wall yawned open and disappeared into the night…

Figure 2 An eyewitness account of the 1976 Guatemala earthquake

The photograph and eyewitness account give us some idea of what it is like to experience an earthquake. Thousands of earthquakes occur every year, but most of these go by unnoticed because they are too small to be felt. What about the big ones? Figure 3 shows the destructive power of earthquakes around the world, measuring them in terms of loss of life. To this must be added the loss of property and the destruction of roads, bridges, and pipelines. Clearly earthquakes can only be described as disasters. But what is an earthquake?

Put simply, an earthquake is the shaking of the ground surface or earth's crust. Measuring an earthquake can be done in two ways. The energy released by an earthquake can be detected on a seismograph (Figure 5). The measurements of the vibrations are then calculated on the Richter Scale. The way the scale works, each level shows a shock 30 times stronger than the previous level – so a level 7 quake is 30 times more powerful than a level 6.

Figure 3

The World's Worst Earthquakes

Location	Year	Casualties
Mexico City, Mexico	1985	10 000
Guatemala	1976	23 000
Yungay, Peru	1970	70 000
North Yemen	1982	23 000
Khurasan, Iran	1968	12 000
Tabas, Iran	1978	25 000
Armenia, USSR	1988	25 000
Quetta, Pakistan	1935	30 000
Tokyo, Japan	1923	100 000
Shaanxi, China	1556	830 000
Jiangsu, China	1920	180 000
Tangshan, China	1976	240 000

Figure 4

The Mercalli Scale

I	Detected only by instruments
II	Very feeble - noticed only by sensitive people
III	Slight - felt by people at rest
IV	Moderate - felt by people who are moving about
V	Rather strong - people wake up, bells ring themselves
VI	Strong - slight damage to buildings
VII	Very strong - walls crack, people panic
VIII	Destructive - chimneys fall
IX	Ruinous - houses fall down
X	Disastrous - many buildings destroyed
XI	Very disastrous - few buildings left standing, ground cracks
XII	Catastrophic - total destruction of buildings, ground badly twisted

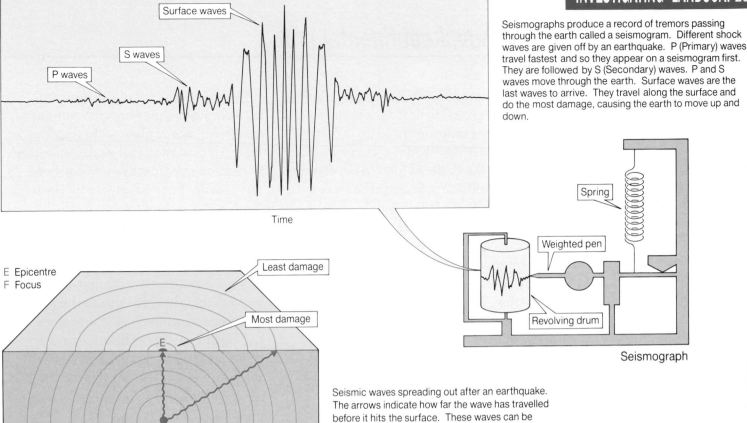

Seismogram

Time

Seismographs produce a record of tremors passing through the earth called a seismogram. Different shock waves are given off by an earthquake. P (Primary) waves travel fastest and so they appear on a seismogram first. They are followed by S (Secondary) waves. P and S waves move through the earth. Surface waves are the last waves to arrive. They travel along the surface and do the most damage, causing the earth to move up and down.

Seismograph

E Epicentre
F Focus

Seismic waves spreading out after an earthquake. The arrows indicate how far the wave has travelled before it hits the surface. These waves can be measured by a seismograph.

Figure 5 A diagram of an earthquake (left) and a seismograph and seismogram (right)

The other way to measure earthquakes is to assess the intensity of the shock by looking at the damage and eyewitness accounts. This is known as the Mercalli Scale, and is shown in Figure 4.

An earthquake begins beneath the surface at its 'focus'. Shock waves spread out in all directions from the focus, as Figure 5 shows. The point directly above the focus on the earth's surface is called the 'epicentre'. This is usually where most damage occurs as it is the place where shock waves are at their most powerful. The readings of the different waves on a seismograph can allow scientists to discover the intensity and the epicentre and focus of the earthquake, and decide whether it is shallow (up to 15 or 20km) or deep-seated (hundreds of kilometres).

But what causes earthquakes? Are we all in danger of them? The next section will help us answer these questions.

Activities

1 Using the photograph of the Armenian earthquake in 1988, draw up a list of words to describe the scene. Now put these words into a short poem or paragraph.
2 Study the Mercalli Scale (Figure 4). Do a series of cartoon drawings for each of Levels I – XII.
3 Using your atlas and a world map outline, locate all of the earthquakes from Figure 3. Remember to give your map a title. You could use different symbols to show the extent of the disaster at each location.
4 Look at your completed map for Activity 3 and see if any pattern has emerged. Where do most earthquakes occur? Are there areas that do not seem to experience earthquakes? Summarise the pattern in a paragraph or two.

5 Plates and continental drift

When someone has been digging a hole, you have probably heard the comment 'Keep going and you'll end up in Australia!' What would a journey to the centre of the earth be like? Well, digging a hole could not provide the answer – the deepest one drilled is only about 11km deep, leaving over 6300km undiscovered! It was the use of seismographs for earthquake detection that unlocked the mystery of the earth's interior. The different wave patterns showed up four layers in the earth. These are illustrated in Figure 1.

Once the make up of the layers had been established, the pattern of oceans and continents was investigated. As early as 1908, Alfred Wegener had put forward the idea of the 'continental jigsaw'. His theory was that the continents fitted together (like the pieces of a jigsaw) and that they had once been a single land mass which had then broken up and drifted apart, but he could not prove this.

In the second half of this century, however, geologists became convinced about the idea of plate tectonics. It is believed that the earth's crust consists of eight major chunks or plates and a few smaller ones, all of which 'float' on the mantle and are moved by the heat of convection currents within the mantle. These are shown by the map in Figure 2. These plates move very slowly, only a few centimetres a year, but it is these movements that give rise to the earthquakes and volcanic eruptions at the earth's surface. These natural disasters tend to occur where plates meet. Plates can move in one of three ways, as shown by the diagrams in Figure 2.

Activities

1 Describe a journey to the centre of the earth from the crust to the inner core. Include details of materials, temperatures, and distances travelled.

2 Using the world map on page 94, trace around the outlines of the continents. Now cut them out and fit them together like a jigsaw. Stick the result in your book. Label it 'Pangea: The Original Earth'.

3 Research idea:
   Conduct some research into the theory of continental drift. Look up Alfred Wegener and Laurasia and Gondwanaland.

4 Compare the map in Figure 2 with your map from Activity 3 in the section on 'Earthquakes!' (pages 36–37). Does this help explain the pattern of earthquakes in terms of plate boundaries? Where are the exceptions? What explanation can you offer for these?

Figure 1 The structure of the earth

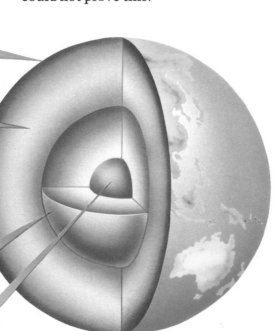

Crust
Solid rock varying in thickness

Mantle
Molten rocks rich in magnesium and silicon

Outer core
Liquid nickel and iron. High pressure and temperature

Inner core
Solid nickel and iron. Very high pressure. Temperatures over 3000°C

Figure 2 The map shows the earth's crustal plates; the diagrams show what happens at the plate margins

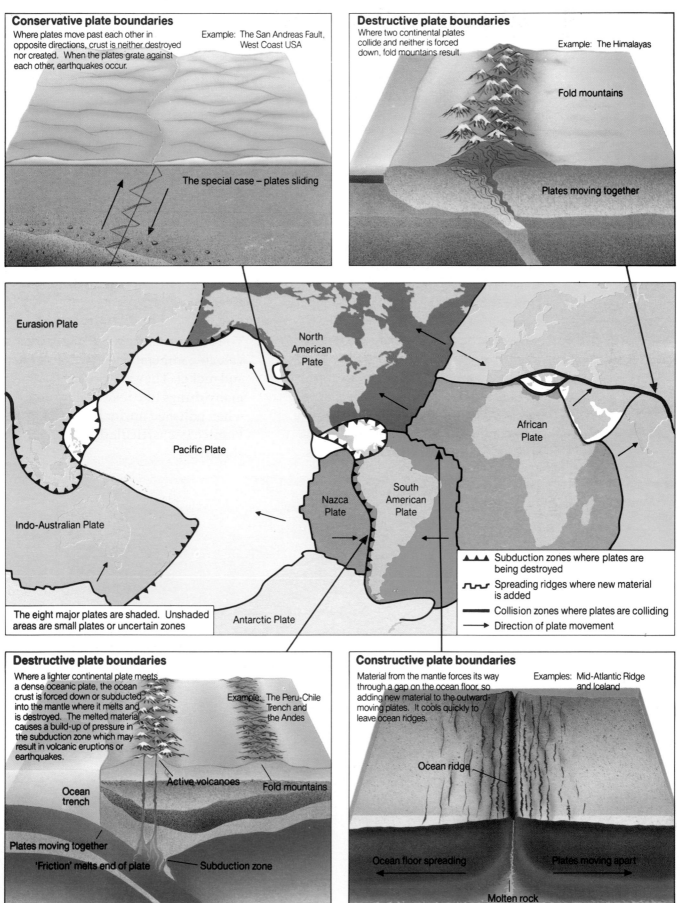

Conservative plate boundaries

Where plates move past each other in opposite directions, crust is neither destroyed nor created. When the plates grate against each other, earthquakes occur.

Example: The San Andreas Fault, West Coast USA

The special case – plates sliding

Destructive plate boundaries

Where two continental plates collide and neither is forced down, fold mountains result.

Example: The Himalayas

Fold mountains

Plates moving together

Eurasion Plate

North American Plate

Pacific Plate

Indo-Australian Plate

African Plate

Nazca Plate

South American Plate

Antarctic Plate

The eight major plates are shaded. Unshaded areas are small plates or uncertain zones

▲▲▲ Subduction zones where plates are being destroyed

ᴨᴨ Spreading ridges where new material is added

━━ Collision zones where plates are colliding

→ Direction of plate movement

Destructive plate boundaries

Where a lighter continental plate meets a dense oceanic plate, the ocean crust is forced down or subducted into the mantle where it melts and is destroyed. The melted material causes a build-up of pressure in the subduction zone which may result in volcanic eruptions or earthquakes.

Example: The Peru-Chile Trench and the Andes

Active volcanoes

Fold mountains

Ocean trench

Plates moving together

'Friction' melts end of plate

Subduction zone

Constructive plate boundaries

Material from the mantle forces its way through a gap on the ocean floor, so adding new material to the outward-moving plates. It cools quickly to leave ocean ridges.

Examples: Mid-Atlantic Ridge and Iceland

Ocean ridge

Ocean floor spreading

Plates moving apart

Molten rock

6 Volcanoes

Figure 1 Three different types of volcano

Shield volcano

Cone volcano

Composite cone volcano

Just looking at a picture of a volcanic eruption like the one in Figure 2 gives you the feeling of power, danger, and beauty. Volcanoes need to be treated with respect! But each volcanic eruption is different and depends both on the type of volcano and, more importantly, on the type of lava involved.

At one end of the scale are the shield or basic cones. These are generally not explosive. They are formed by runny lava at about 1000°C spreading out over a large area, so creating the gentle slopes of the cones. Where the lava is slightly cooler (about 700°C) and thicker (viscous), acid cones are formed with steep sides through explosions of gas and ash. In between these two are a whole range of composite cones made up of a mixture of ash and lava layers.

These different types of volcano are shown in Figure 1.

Throughout the world there are some 500 volcanoes which are still active (Figure 3). In many of these places the negative effects of a possible eruption have been outweighed by the positive effects that volcanoes can bring. These benefits include:

1 Soils.
   Volcanic soils are rich and fertile so many people like to farm on or near volcanoes.

2 Minerals.
   Volcanic rocks are full of useful or valuable minerals like gold, copper, and nickel. They are also used for many things like road building or, when polished up, for buildings. Pumice is a particularly excellent abrasive.

Figure 2
Kilauea, Hawaii

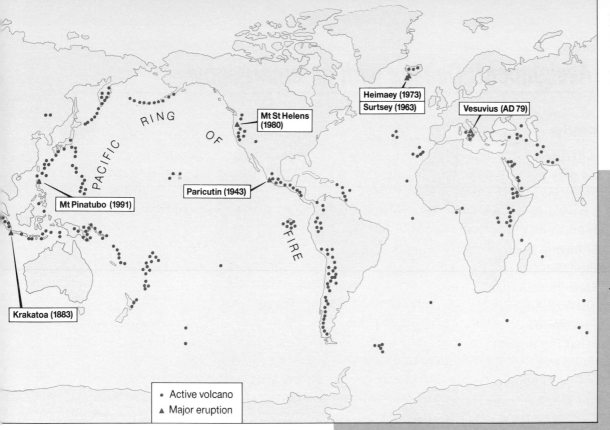

Heimaey (1973)
Surtsey (1963)
Mt St Helens (1980)
Vesuvius (AD 79)
Mt Pinatubo (1991)
Paricutin (1943)
Krakatoa (1883)

PACIFIC RING OF FIRE

- Active volcano
▲ Major eruption

Figure 3 The world distribution of volcanoes, with some famous eruptions labelled

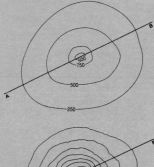

3 Geothermal energy.
There is a vast potential source of renewable energy from the hot water springs near volcanoes. Many countries like New Zealand, Iceland, Japan, and Italy are now developing this resource.

4 Tourism.
Because of the growth of this industry, countries like Iceland are now exploiting the beautiful scenery and spectacular sites of geysers and crater lakes. Curiously, the hotels around Mount Etna are always full if an eruption is predicted!

Due to these positive benefits and the fact that we are increasingly able to predict volcanic eruptions, vast numbers of people continue to live in areas around active volcanoes. However, there is still a lot of uncertainty, particularly as more people are killed by tsunami (tidal waves), mudflows, and nuée ardente ('fiery clouds' of gas and ash) resulting from an eruption than are ever killed by the lava and eruption itself.

Activities

1 Compare the map of plate boundaries on page 39 with the world map showing volcanoes (Figure 3).
a) Is the distribution of volcanoes similar to the distribution of earthquakes?
b) Which plate boundaries are particularly responsible for volcano activity? Make a list of them.

2 Look at the two contour patterns above of two different volcano types. Produce a cross-section from A to B for each one and then decide (a) what type of cone it is and (b) how it was formed. Label your cross-sections to show the main features and the differences between them.

3 Research idea:
The map in Figure 3 shows a number of well-documented volcanic eruptions. Working in small groups or as a class, research the stories behind these eruptions using library books. Now bring your findings together, either as a class display or simply as a reporting-back session.

4 Imagine you are the Minister for Tourism in Iceland. Put together a brochure which advertises the spectacular holidays available in your country (a visit to a travel agent will help here).

7 Assignment: Dealing with an emergency

Background information

When you think about natural disasters, there is a tendency to conclude that little or nothing can be done to prevent the damage and loss of life. But is this really the case? This section shows how California, a state on the West Coast of the USA, has tackled the danger of earthquakes that comes from living on the San Andreas Fault. They have adopted the '3Ps' policy (Figures 1–3) so that the impact of a quake is brought down to a minimum.

Figure 1

Predict

The drawing below shows a number of ways in which earth tremors can be measured. Changes in these measurements can be used to forecast when and where a quake will occur and steps can then be taken to deal with it.

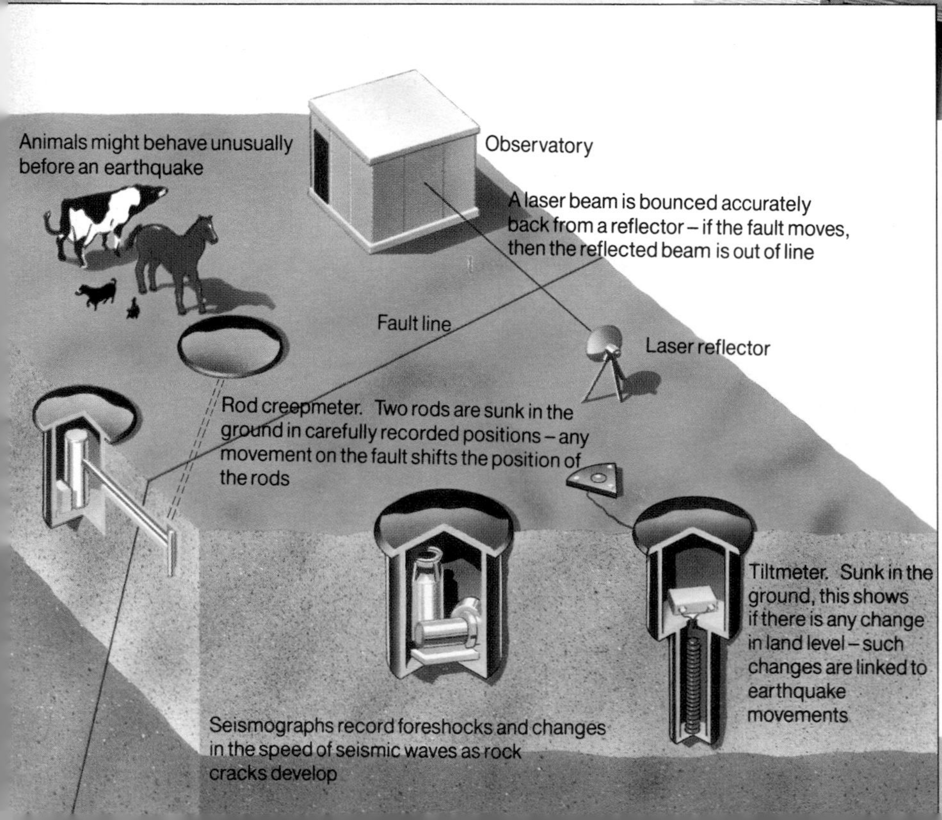

Protect

After the Armenian earthquake in 1988 an engineer commented 'Earthquakes don't kill, buildings do.' Designing buildings so that they are earthquake-proof can do a great deal to lessen the loss of life. The photo above shows the earthquake-proof Transamerican Pyramid which withstood the 1989 quake in San Francisco. Creating triangles within buildings gives them extra strength - a triangle is a very stable geometric shape. Simpler and cheaper methods include lightweight, interconnected yet flexible wooden structures.

Figure 2

Animals might behave unusually before an earthquake

Observatory

A laser beam is bounced accurately back from a reflector – if the fault moves, then the reflected beam is out of line

Fault line

Laser reflector

Rod creepmeter. Two rods are sunk in the ground in carefully recorded positions – any movement on the fault shifts the position of the rods

Tiltmeter. Sunk in the ground, this shows if there is any change in land level – such changes are linked to earthquake movements

Seismographs record foreshocks and changes in the speed of seismic waves as rock cracks develop

Before the quake

Develop a family earthquake plan. Prepare yourself, your family, and your home by completing the activities on this checklist.

- Decide how and where your family will reunite if separated.
- Choose an out-of-state friend or relative that separated family members can call after the quake to report their whereabouts and condition.
- Know the safe spots in each room: under sturdy tables, desks, or against inside walls.

- Know the danger spots: windows, mirrors, hanging objects, fire-places, and unsecured furniture.
- Conduct practice drills. Physically place yourself in safe locations.
- Learn first aid.
- Keep a list of emergency phone numbers.
- Learn how to shut off gas, water, and electricity in case the lines are damaged.
- Check chimneys, roofs, walls, and foundations for stability.
- Keep breakables and heavy objects on bottom shelves, and secure heavy tall furniture that can topple.
- Maintain emergency food, water, and other supplies, including a flashlight, a portable battery-operated radio, extra batteries, medicines, first aid kit, and clothing.

During the quake

If **indoors**, stay there. Get under a table or stand in a corner.

If **outdoors**, get into an open area away from trees, buildings, and power lines.

If in a **high-rise building**, stay away from windows and outside walls. Do not use elevators.

If **driving**, pull over to the side of the road and stop. Avoid overpasses and power lines. Stay inside until the shaking is over.

If in a **crowded public place**, do not rush for the doors. Move away from display shelves containing objects that could fall.

After the quake

Check for injuries. Apply first aid. Do not move seriously injured individuals unless they are in immediate danger. Do not use the telephone immediately unless there is a serious injury or fire.

Hunt for hazards:

- Check for gas and water leaks, broken electrical wiring or sewage lines.
- Check buildings for cracks and damage, including roof, chimneys, and foundations.

- Check food and water supplies. Emergency water may be obtained from water heaters, melted ice cubes, toilet tanks, and canned vegetables.
- Turn on your portable radio for instructions and radio reports.
- Do not use your vehicle unless there is an emergency. Keep the streets clear for emergency vehicles.
- Be prepared for aftershocks.
- Stay calm and lend a hand to others.

Prepare

If people know how to behave before, during, and after the disaster they are more likely to survive. The 'Beat the Quake' guide shown here is issued free and is available on the counters of shops in the area.

Figure 3

Your assignment

It is clear from the background information that California is taking the threat of earthquakes seriously, but many areas that are in just as much danger have done little to put together a 3Ps plan. You are going to take on the role of the Office of Emergency Services for a developing country. You will need to work in a small group for this assignment. The Work Programme sets out what your group has to do.

Work Programme

You office has been given the responsibility of drawing up a 3Ps plan for the country. Remember that developing countries have lower levels of literacy than California and less money to spend. With this in mind, complete these tasks:

- What are your prediction measures? Where will they be? How many? What types? Map out your plans.
- Design an earthquake survival guide for your people so that they are prepared.
- Design and build some new earthquake-proof buildings for your capital city for protection. You may use cardboard or building materials available from the Design and Technology Department. Try experimenting with straws or 'Lego'. The possibilities are endless.
- Now present your group's 3Ps plan to the rest of the class who will assess the success of your measures.

8 *What do people think?*

Figure 1 A poem

Seascape

The waves come pelting in like porpoises
Coming in white curved profiles or pounding in full face
Like sheets of melting metal. And every spray
Shakes up a rainbow, while far out the heaving water
Rushes to repeat the swell in a stranger fuller way
As the milky foam founders and suppresses our voices.

Crash after crash and colour and green consistency of white waves.
Stray salmon and sea trout trapped in swaying nets.
Again the whole attack of the sea, formidable and fearsome,
Splashing against the squares of stone, dazzling like a snowstorm,
Blasting up the debris and howling at the dumb
Humans who observe the liquid sea in silent droves.

Alan Bold

A poem, a photograph, a painting, and a book – four ways of describing a scene. Each one gives us one person's view of a place. Would everyone agree on what the place is like? What are the things in any landscape that make it interesting or pleasant or useful to us?

One way we could think about or evaluate a landscape is to decide on the sort of words we would use to describe it.

One way of doing this is explained in the Skills Box (Figure 5). The technique asks you to think carefully about your view of a landscape and then to choose between pairs of words with opposite meanings. The proper name for this technique is the 'bi-polar semantic differential test'!

Figure 2 A photograph: Sydney Harbour

Figure 3 A painting: Wensleydale in the Yorkshire Dales by His Royal Highness The Prince of Wales

Figure 4 An extract from a book

CHAPTER 1
THE PURCHASE

I first saw Dyffryn in a November gale. As I rounded a spur of a hill to turn into the long valley the full power of the storm caught the car. An abandoned lorry, blown onto its side, half blocked the road, and as I crept past it an eddying gust swooped down, plucked at the car's hood, and ripped it backward till it streamed raggedly behind. The rain was being driven horizontally, and struck on the windscreen. It poured in torrents over the bonnet, but left me dry.

The entrance to Dyffryn valley is guarded by two lakes. The left wall of the valley is the long hump of Moel Siabod, and the right wall, higher and more rough, is the Glyders. Across the head of the valley stand Snowdon and her satellites, like maidens hand in hand, barring the way out. But on that first day wild flurries of rain and mist shut out the skylines, and the steep, rocky slopes reared upward till they were swallowed by the clouds. Every now and again the clouds were rent like parted curtains, to reveal yet higher hills, from whose every hollow and gully streamed creaming water. The wind raced like a live thing about the upper slopes; sometimes it carried bodily away a whole waterfall, so that for a moment not a drop would spill over the brink.

The surface of the twin lakes was whipped into vicious white horses. Along the shores huge boulders lay scattered haphazard, as if untidy giant children had fled for shelter, leaving their marbles where they lay.

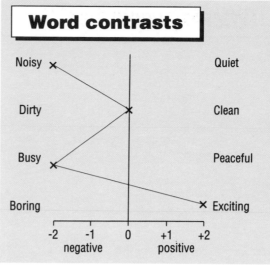

Word contrasts

Step 1 Choose a number of adjectives and their opposites to describe a scene.

Step 2 Arrange them on a graph, as shown.

Step 3 Now "score" the scene. For example, if it is slightly noisy score - 1, but if it is very noisy score - 2. Mark each score with a cross.

Step 4 Join up the crosses to make a profile for your score.

Step 5 Repeat for another scene, or for another person's scores. Use different colours for each profile.

Figure 5 Skills Box

Activities

1 Look at Figures 1–4, and copy and complete this table.

Figure	How is it described?	What type of landscape is it?	What would you do if you were there right now?
1	Poem	?????	?????

2 Now compare your answers with those of someone else. Did you agree? What about the rest of the class? Write a paragraph to explain your findings.

3 Work with a partner. Both of you should read the Skills Box carefully. You are going to do your own word contrast test on the landscapes described in Figures 1–4.
a) Make your own list of ten word pairs. You can use the pairs in the Skills Box as a start and then add more of your own. Try to choose words that can be used about many different types of landscape.
b) Now draw a separate graph for each landscape as the Skills Box explains.
c) Write about what your completed graphs tell you about your views of the four landscapes.

4 Try the same test for an area you know well – around the school perhaps or your home neighbourhood or another place you know well. What does the test tell you about how you view that landscape?

5 Different people using the same word contrast test about the same area will often get different results. Why?

1 Different uses

Figure 1 Under pressure!

Figure 2 The location of the Peak National Park

Twenty million day visitors a year, up to 100 000 cars on a fine Sunday, not to mention the 40 000 people that live and work there. No wonder the Peak National Park is under pressure from the different needs of its many different users. The cartoon in Figure 1 tries to show the results of this pressure.

From early times, metals and minerals like lead, copper, zinc, and silver have been mined in the area. Now the biggest industry is limestone quarrying. Each day enough limestone to cover a football pitch to a depth of four metres is removed. This amounts to 24 million tons a year, 6 million tons of which comes from inside the National Park itself. The limestone is used in a wide variety of ways (Figure 4) and so it is not surprising that the demand for it is still growing. There are now a number of quarries and processing plants coping with this need,

both inside and outside the National Park. How do people react to having a limestone quarry like the one in Figure 3 in their locality? And what about the processing plants that prepare the limestone for use? How do these activities fit in with tourism in the Park? Imagine the heavy lorries churning their way along winding narrow roads, the noise that comes from blasting and processing, and the dust pollution in the air.

It seems a difficult task to balance the needs of industry with the needs of tourism, but that is the job of the National Park Authority. Somehow, different users have to be allowed the freedom to gain what they require, whether it is work or recreation, without damaging the future of the Park. This is also the case in many other places, and is where landscape protection comes in.

Figure 3 A limestone quarry in the Peak National Park

Figure 4 What limestone is used for

Roadstone	62%
Cement	30%
Chemical industry	4%
Agriculture	2%
Iron & steel	2%

Activities

1 Look at the cartoon in Figure 1. Make a list of all the different types of park user. Put alongside each user their reason for being there. You could write up your answers in a table like the one shown here:

User	Reason
Sheep farmer	Works there, lives there.

2 Figure 4 shows the different uses of limestone. Draw a pie graph to show this information. Then try to explain why each of these uses is still growing (for example, more roadstone is used because we are building more roads).

3 Here (right) are a number of people and what they think about the quarry in their village. Match up the person with their opinion.

4 A decision has to be taken about how the limestone industry is going to develop in the future. These are the four alternatives:

(i) All quarries in the Park to be closed down.
(ii) No more new quarries in the Park.
(iii) Any new quarries to be on existing sites.
(iv) No restrictions on quarries as they are needed to meet demand.

For each of the alternatives, say whether you agree or disagree with it and give reasons why.

Person	Opinion
A Quarry owner	**1** 'The local people have few local job opportunities. This is one of them.'
B Village resident who works elsewhere	**2** 'We needed a new site as we expanded. This one is ideal.'
C Village resident who works at quarry	**3** 'The quarry is the reason I live here. It's my job.'
D Local councillor	**4** 'I expected the village to be peaceful and quiet. Now we have to put up with all this.'

2 National Parks

If we look back on the 1980s we can see that 'green' issues have become major talking points. From Prince Charles to 'Blue Peter', the protection of our landscape is seen as important. But it is worth noting that certain areas have been protected for over forty years, so green ideas are nothing new! After the Second World War, the government decided to create National Parks.

Figure 1 Areas of protected landscape in the UK

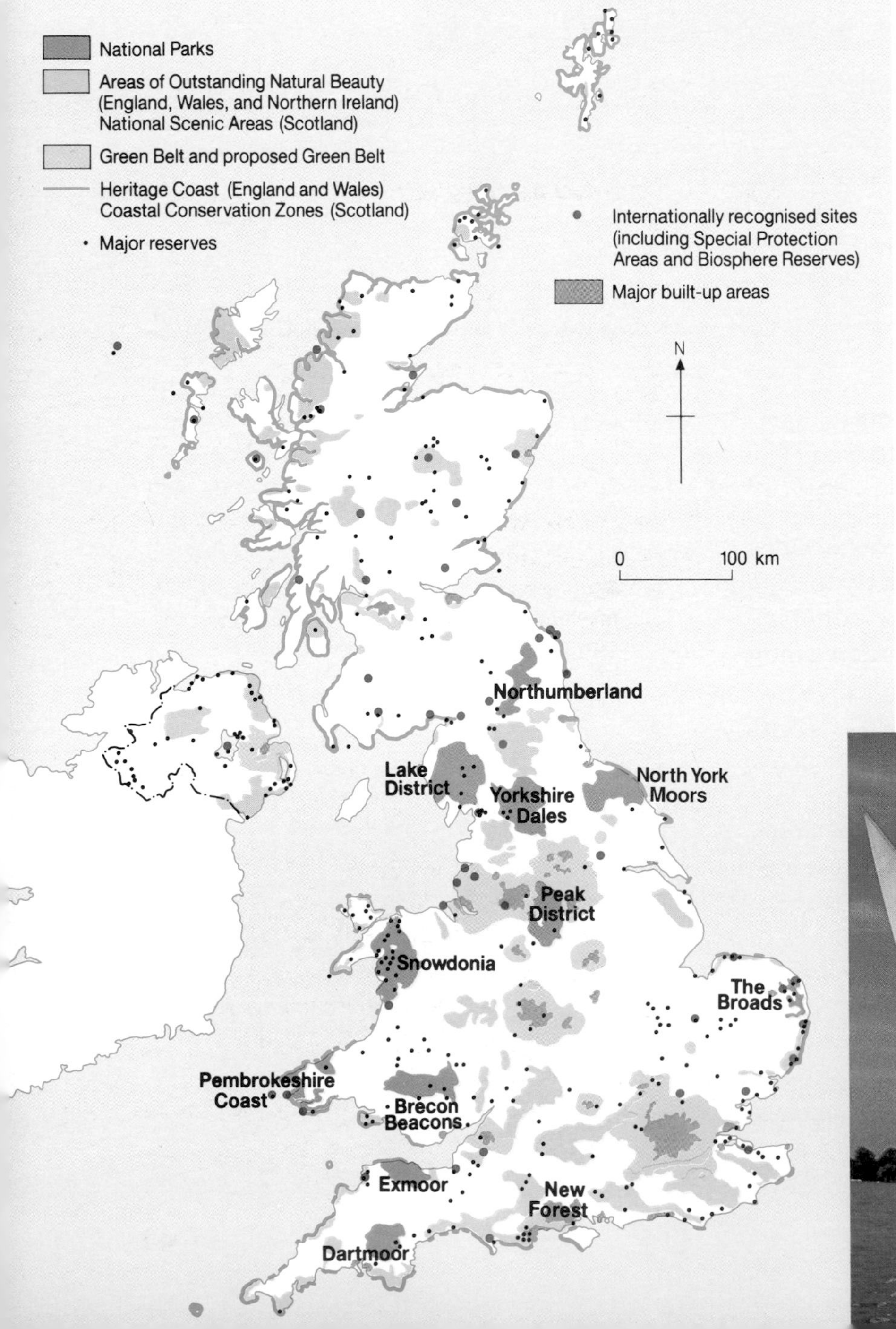

There are now twelve National Parks (Figure 1) and they cover over ten per cent of England and Wales. The National Parks aim to do four things:

1 Preserve the landscape;
2 Allow public recreation;
3 Look after wildlife and historic buildings;
4 Keep the local economy going.

The parks are usually controlled by local authorities, although the Lake District, Peak District, and Norfolk Broads have a special planning board. As well as these large areas, there are many other protected areas, as Figure 1 shows. These include Areas of Outstanding Natural Beauty (AONBs), Country Parks, Nature Reserves, Heritage Coasts and, in Scotland, National Scenic Areas. Some of the smaller areas are protected for a particular reason, like a rare bird or flower. Sometimes the job of looking after or managing the protected areas is given to agencies like the National Conservancy Council or the Forestry Commission or the National Trust. There are difficulties though.

Key

■ National Parks

▨ Areas of Outstanding Natural Beauty (England, Wales, and Northern Ireland) National Scenic Areas (Scotland)

▨ Green Belt and proposed Green Belt

— Heritage Coast (England and Wales) Coastal Conservation Zones (Scotland)

• Major reserves

● Internationally recognised sites (including Special Protection Areas and Biosphere Reserves)

▨ Major built-up areas

N

0   100 km

Northumberland
Lake District
Yorkshire Dales
North York Moors
Peak District
Snowdonia
The Broads
Pembrokeshire Coast
Brecon Beacons
Exmoor
New Forest
Dartmoor

Figure 2 Wherries on the Norfolk Broads

In the National Parks the biggest landowners are usually private or the Ministry of Defence, as Figures 3 and 4 show. This can make it complicated to always achieve what is wanted, but the more land that becomes protected in some way, the greater chance we all have of enjoying different types of scenery and varying environments.

Figure 3 Who owns the land in the Peak National Park

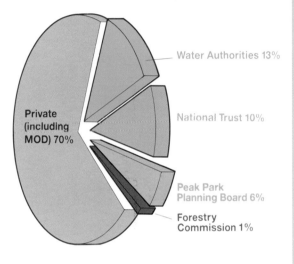

Figure 4 The percentage of land owned by the Ministry of Defence in three National Parks

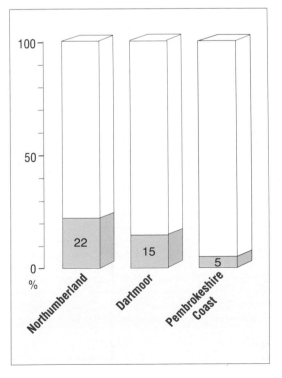

Activities

1 Using Figure 1 and your atlas to help you, copy and complete this table showing the characteristics of National Parks.

Name of National Park	Highland or lowland	Name of nearest city or urban area
Peak District	Highland (Pennines)	Sheffield

2 Now answer the following questions.
a) What type of scenery does your table suggest is most common in National Parks? Why might this make them attractive to visitors?
b) Are all National Parks close to areas with large populations? What does this mean for the type of visitors they can expect?

3 Each one of the National Parks has a symbol for publicity and advertising. Four are shown below.

The Norfolk Broads is one of the newest parks. Design a symbol for the Broads Authority to use. The photograph in Figure 2 might give you a few ideas.

4 Research idea:
Conduct a piece of research into another type of protected area (not National Parks). Find out who controls the area, what can and does go on, and whether or not the protection is successful. You could present your findings as a written report or you could give a talk to your class.

3 Local conservation

In order to make the news, conservation schemes are usually large-scale and involve lots of money, but often more success comes from smaller and less well known projects. Figures 1 and 2 are two views of the Farthinghoe Nature Reserve in South Northamptonshire. Looking at Figure 1, it is obvious that the reserve used to be part of a railway line. This is called the 'Old Cutting' on the map in Figure 3. The railway was closed down in 1963. Two years later the county council bought the site and began using part of it for dumping household rubbish. In 1983, 60 000 tons of rubbish later, the infill was covered with topsoil.

In 1984, the council made the eight-acre site a nature reserve. Figure 2 shows what part of the reserve looks like now. This is the part previously used for dumping rubbish, and is called the 'Plateau' on the map in Figure 3. The whole area is being looked after (managed) to allow different habitats to develop naturally. Some things, like the tree planting on the Plateau, are long-term projects and it will be many years before the trees are fully grown. It will also be a while before much more needs to be done. Other things, like the pond, need a lot of looking after all the time. As well as being managed for habitat development, the reserve is also trying to encourage the public to use its facilities. The map in Figure 3 shows the ways this has and will be done. The future of a place like this depends very much on the work of wardens, local conservation groups, schools, and other volunteers. In a few years a lot can be achieved. But conservation schemes of all types need continual support if our countryside habitats are to remain protected.

Figure 1

Figure 2

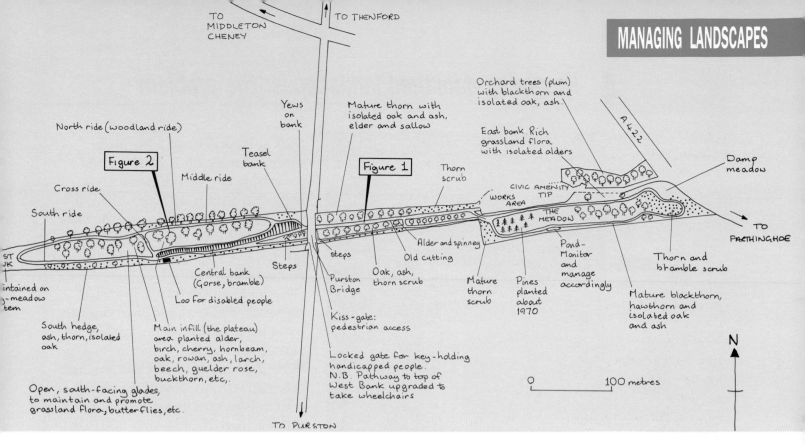

Figure 3 Farthinghoe Nature Reserve

Item	Cost (£s)
Toilets, display cabin with information	5000
An audio-visual presentation about the reserve	3000
Producing publicity material	2000
Laying out a nature trail	3000
Building a car park	7000
Employing another part-time warden	4000
Tree-planting schemes	4500

Figure 4 How the county council grant of £8000 could be spent

Activities

1 Make a tracing of the map of the reserve (Figure 3) and colour it in to show the different habitat areas.

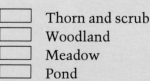

Thorn and scrub
Woodland
Meadow
Pond

2 Two groups of people using the reserve are horse riders and disabled visitors. Use the map to explain what has been done to allow enjoyment of the facilities by both of these groups.

3 Look at Figure 4. It gives details of how your council grant of £8000 for the coming year could be spent. Working in a small group, agree how to spend the money. Then elect a speaker to explain the reasons for your group decision.

4 Research idea:
Look in your local newspaper to see if there are any conservation schemes in your area. Find out about the site and how it is managed. (You could even visit or offer your help!)

4 Restoring damaged landscapes: the problem

Figure 1 A damaged landscape

Figure 2 The same landscape, but restored

Look at Figures 1 and 2. We might expect scenes such as these to have come from two very different areas because the landscape is so different. In fact, these photographs are of the same place! The photograph in Figure 2 was taken just a few years after the photograph in Figure 1.

Figure 1 shows how the human activities of mining and quarrying can scar a landscape. Over the last 200 years, in areas like this one in Derbyshire, minerals such as coal have been extracted to provide the raw materials and power for our industries and transport.

Mining in South Derbyshire alone grew steadily, as Figure 4 shows. And as it grew, the landscape changed. Sometimes the mining itself was responsible for the 'scar' as the land was 'eaten away'. However, the main problem was the waste material that was produced. It was often difficult to find a good use for the waste, so it was stockpiled in huge spoil heaps. Figure 1 shows such a heap.

As mining continued, so did the growth of waste. But in the last thirty years coal-mining has largely disappeared in South Derbyshire, as Figure 4 also shows. This has presented an ideal opportunity to do something about the scarred landscape and the waste.

In the example provided by Figures 1 and 2, the spoil heap has simply been removed. In other instances, spoil heaps have been landscaped, covered with topsoil, and planted with trees and grass. Damaged landscapes need not remain eyesores. Indeed, they can be put to new uses, as the next section shows.

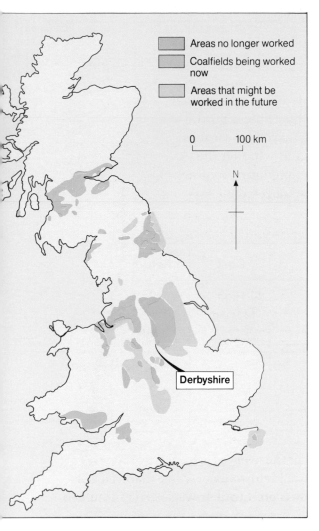

Figure 3 Britain's coalfields. They all face the problem of restoring damaged landscapes

Mine	Opened	Closed
Church Gresley	1812	1967
Rawdon	1821	1989
Granville	1823	1967
Measham	1850	1986
Reservoir	1851	1948
Swadlincote	1852	1965
Netherseal	1855	1947
Donisthorpe	1857	1990
Stanhope Drift	1859	1966
Cadley Hill	1860	1988
Bretby	1872	1962

Figure 4 The opening and closing of mines in South Derbyshire

Activities

1 Use the dates in Figure 4 to draw a graph showing the growth and decline of coal-mining in South Derbyshire. Group the years in decades on the horizontal axis and draw bars for the number of mines open. The axes below show you how.

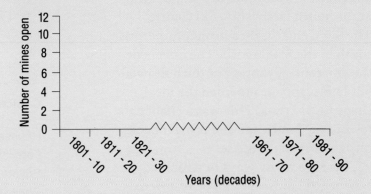

2 Copy and complete the following paragraph which describes your graph.

Coal-mining in South Derbyshire first began in _____ . The industry grew very quickly in the decade _____ , with _____ new mines opening. The industry remained stable for the next _____ years. After the Second World War, mines started to close, with five mines closing in the decade _____ . The last mine in the area closed in _____ , _____ years after mining first began.

3 The 1:25 000 Ordnance Survey map in the next section is of the South Derbyshire area. Place a tracing overlay on the right hand side of the map and then identify the following land uses with three different colours.

 Housing
Industry (all mine workings)
Other uses

4 Now try and describe the pattern of land use in the area shown by your tracing. How likely is landscape damage in an area like this?

5 Restoring damaged landscapes: the solution

Imagine you were standing in square 3019 on the map in Figure 1. According to the map evidence, what sort of landscape would you be in? Now look at the top photograph. This is in square 3019. These people are dry-slope skiing at the South Derbyshire Ski Centre. The Ski Centre is on a former mine site south of the B5005 road. The buyers of the site took advantage of the hollowed-out landscape – it provided the ideal shape for ski runs. This was a chance to restore the landscape and bring it back into money-making use.

There are many ways in which a damaged landscape can be restored. The decision as to what can or should be done with an area is usually based on the rules of economics. In other words, will the money paid out to restore the site (the cost) be more or less than the expected money to be gained from its new use (the return). Schemes will go ahead only if the returns are expected to be higher than the costs.

Sometimes, however, the rules of economics are ignored if the result of the restoration is thought to be good for the area and the people living there. The bottom photograph shows another area of square 3019. Here a spoil heap has been flattened, grassed over, and turned into a football pitch, this time by the local council. Whatever the choice, it is generally agreed that something rather than nothing should be done to restore our damaged landscapes.

Activities

1 Copy and complete this table which shows the possible choices for the restoration of damaged landscapes. You must work out whether the answer is 'high', 'medium', or 'low'. Some have already been done for you.

Choice	Cost	Return
Houses	High	?
Farmland	Medium	?
Private leisure	?	High
Public leisure	?	Low
Woodland	Low	?
Water	?	?
Industrial estate	?	High

2 Now try and rank these choices in order of economic performance. Remember that a high return on a low cost is best.

3 Write a paragraph to explain why certain land uses are more popular than others when land is being restored.

4 You have been given the task of restoring the area around Donisthorpe (the last colliery to close in the region) in square 3114. Produce your ideas for this. You could include sketches, plans, maps, and a written account to illustrate your scheme.

Figure 1 Part of South Derbyshire, from an Ordnance Survey 1:25 000 map. The photos show restored landscapes

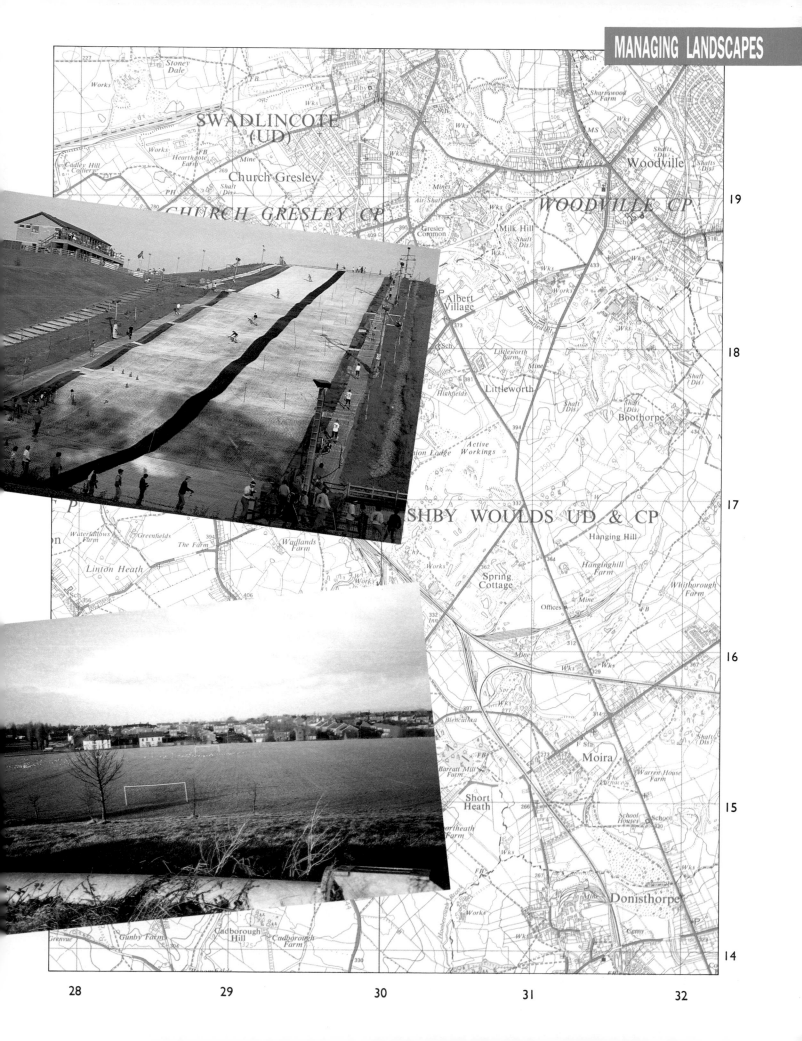

6 Tackling damage from leisure

Figure 2 Some of the changes that have affected recreation

1966

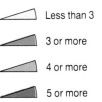

1971

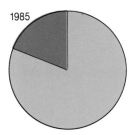

1985

Number of weeks paid holiday per year

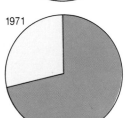

Less than 3

3 or more

4 or more

5 or more

Figure 1 Ah . . . peace and quiet . . . .

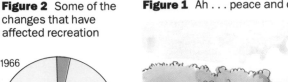

How do you spend your time? A recent survey has shown that after eating, sleeping, travelling, and working we still have five hours each day to do our own thing. What is more, this figure increases at weekends and in holiday periods. So, what do we do with this time? Many of us use it for recreation and leisure, but of what sort? Figure 3 gives a summary of how recreation time is spent. The problem is that lots of us find ourselves all together in the same place at the same time. The cartoonist in Figure 1 has tried to show this and has certainly succeeded in making a point. The concentration of people in popular places has led to these places

becoming known as 'honeypots' – places attracting swarms of visitors all wanting to enjoy the same thing.

Honeypots have only become common over the last forty years. This is because our lifestyle has changed considerably in that time. Some of these changes are shown in Figure 2. One of the biggest problems is that the honeypots can end up being damaged through over-use. This certainly seems strange. The very people who choose a particular place for its peace and quiet and the chance to get away from it all end up helping to create a situation like that shown in the cartoon. Not another Bank Holiday!

Figure 3 How most people spend their recreation time

Where?	Within 80km of home; a few places take most visitors
How?	By car. Most do not move more than 100m from their car!
When?	Summer; Sunday, 3.30 - 5.30p.m.
Why?	Most are pleasure driving

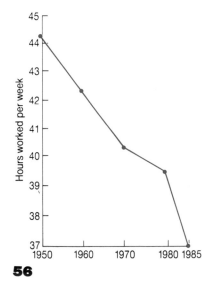

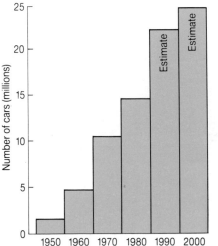

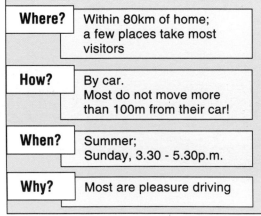

Figure 4 Dovedale in the Peak National Park – a famous honeypot

Activities

1 Use the graphs in Figure 2 to match the following 'heads and tails' sentences. Then copy out the completed and correct sentences.

Heads
▶ Car ownership has increased from 1.5 million in 1950 to over 20 million in 1990 . . .
▶ Annual paid holiday has increased . . .
▶ The number of hours worked per week has decreased . . .

Tails
▶ . . . from over 44 in 1950 to 37 in 1985, giving more time for leisure.
▶ . . . giving time and money for leisure.
▶ . . . so that more people can travel further more easily.

2 Here are two people from the cartoon in Figure 1. Try and think of a suitable comment to describe their feelings.

3 The photograph in Figure 4 is of Dovedale in the Peak National Park, a well-known honeypot.
a) Describe the scene shown in the photo.
b) What evidence is there of problems caused by pressure of visitors?
c) Suggest ways in which this pressure, or any other pressure, might be eased in locations such as this.

7 Assignment: Making a management plan

Figure 1 Information about the Oxwich Bay habitat areas

The beach

A very attractive, gently sloping, sandy beach. Car park, toilets, cafes, and kiosks are available.

Problems

Many visitors for water sports in summer. Litter from picnics and barbeques. Cars, 4x4s, and trailers on beach when car park is full. Bathers in danger from boats and surfboards.

Management possibilities
● More staff, especially in summer (e.g. lifeguards)
● Put flags out for bathing area
● More litter bins
● Ban vehicles from beach
● Increase car parking charges

Sand dunes

A large area behind the beach. The dunes have different amounts of vegetation cover. There are many species, some rare.

Problems

Public trample over dunes, eroding them. Bracken overtakes all other species, 'blocking out' rare varieties.

Management possibilities
● Fence-off dunes as in photograph
● Wardens patrol dunes/put up signs to keep public off
● Mow bracken 2-4 times a year
● Use goats to graze on dunes
● Use visitors centre to give public understanding of habitats

Marshland

A freshwater marsh behind the dunes. The area is 'man-made' as it was once a salt-marsh. Here is the richest variety of species, both plants and birds.

Problems
Water level must be kept high and fresh. Public disturb birdlife and trample on marsh plants.

Management possibilities
● Control water level with weirs and sluice gates
● Public use boardwalks or only allowed in to marsh on guided tours
● Public use bird hides

Woodland

Mainly on slopes behind the bay. These trees have grown since the end of limestone quarrying in the last 200 years.

Problems

Sycamore grows too quickly and dominates the others, especially oak.

Management possibilities
● Coppice the sycamore regularly
● Use the wood for sale

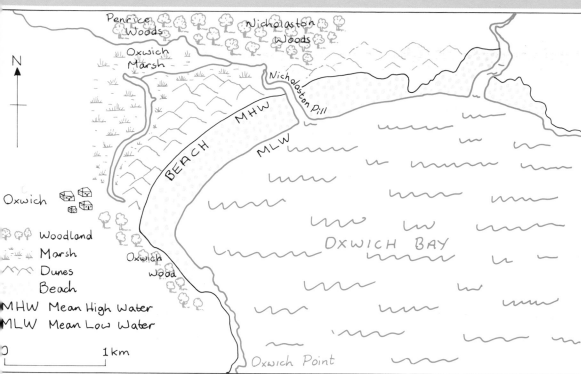

Figure 2 Map showing the Oxwich Bay habitat areas

- Woodland
- Marsh
- Dunes
- Beach
- MHW Mean High Water
- MLW Mean Low Water

0   1km

Background information

Oxwich Bay in South Wales is a National Nature Reserve (NNR). The reserve is owned by the Nature Conservancy Council (NNC), which is given its money by the government.

Oxwich Bay is a NNR because of the different types of landscape which are found there, as shown in Figures 1 and 2. Each landscape provides a different habitat for animals, plants, or people. The task of the council is to manage the area so that the plants and animals are protected while, at the same time, people are allowed to use as much of the area as possible.

Your assignment

Work in groups of three or four people for this assignment. Your group has the job of producing a management plan for the Oxwich Bay National Nature Reserve. What you have to do is outlined in the Work Programme. You have been provided (Figure 1) with a description of each habitat, its particular problems, and some of the ideas to preserve it.

Oxwich Bay ——

Work Programme

- The NCC will need a written report explaining your plans for each habitat so that you obtain your grant. Study the management possibilities carefully and then make your recommendations for each area.
- Many visitors to the reserve will want to know all about it. Using the descriptions, photographs, and map *either* produce a number of posters for a display at a visitors centre or car park kiosk;
  or produce a tape commentary or leaflet which could be used for a guided tour of the reserve.

59

1 Population changes

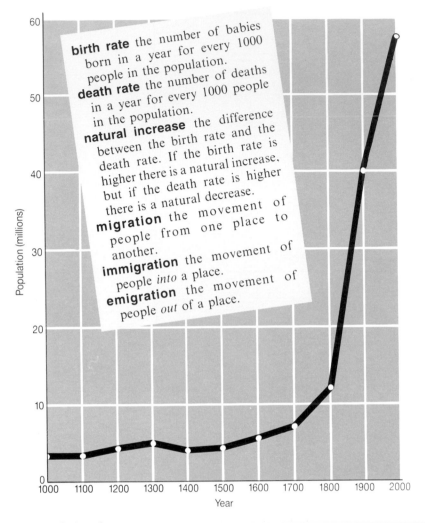

birth rate the number of babies born in a year for every 1000 people in the population.

death rate the number of deaths in a year for every 1000 people in the population.

natural increase the difference between the birth rate and the death rate. If the birth rate is higher there is a natural increase, but if the death rate is higher there is a natural decrease.

migration the movement of people from one place to another.

immigration the movement of people *into* a place.

emigration the movement of people *out* of a place.

Do you know how many people currently live in the United Kingdom? The answer is over 57 million. As you can see from the graph in Figure 1, the population has risen dramatically over the last 150 years. It may continue to rise, but much more slowly. The reasons for these changes in population are outlined below.

The population of an area or country can change in a number of ways. Imagine a man and a woman, stranded on a deserted island. The population of the island is therefore two. Four different events could happen to change the population of the island:

1 The couple have a baby;
2 One of them dies;
3 Other people arrive on the island;
4 The man and/or woman leaves the island.

For a country to calculate its population and explain any changes, it has to look at all four of these events. And, of course, it has to look at them on a much larger scale!

Figure 1 (graph, above) Population growth in the UK, 1000–2000

Figure 2 (inset, above) Some common population terms explained

Figure 3 People have always migrated. The flood of millions of people into the USA during the late nineteenth and early twentieth centuries was one of the great migrations of history. This photo shows new arrivals at Ellis Island, New York, lining up to have their papers examined

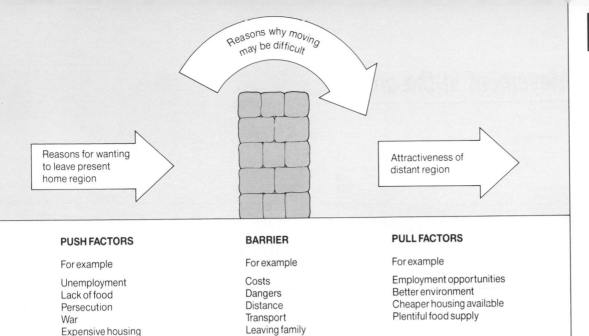

PUSH FACTORS

For example

Unemployment
Lack of food
Persecution
War
Expensive housing

BARRIER

For example

Costs
Dangers
Distance
Transport
Leaving family

PULL FACTORS

For example

Employment opportunities
Better environment
Cheaper housing available
Plentiful food supply

Figure 4 The push-pull factors causing migration

There are four major types of migration:

1. Intra-urban migration occurs when people move within the same city or town.
2. Rural-urban migration involves huge numbers of people, particularly in developing countries. People move from the countryside to the city in search of jobs and better opportunities.
3. Urban-rural migration has become a growing trend in many developed countries. People are choosing to leave the overcrowded and polluted cities to live in the countryside. Here, housing is usually cheaper, and modern transport means that it is fairly easy to commute to the city for work.
4. International migration occurs when people leave their home country to live in another country. The decision to move is, in some cases, forced upon them because of war, famine, or persecution in their native country.

The causes of migration are summarised in the simple push-pull diagram in Figure 4.

Activities

1. Have you ever moved house? Make a list of the push and pull factors that resulted in you moving.
2. Look at the graph in Figure 1 showing population growth in the United Kingdom.
   a) Copy and complete the table below by working out the population in each of the years shown.

Year	Population (millions)	Year	Population (millions)
1000		1800	
1200		1900	
1400		2000	
1600			

   b) Suggest some possible reasons for the dramatic drop in population around 1348.
   c) When did the population begin to increase at a rapid rate?
   d) Why do you think the population started to increase?
3. Use the figures below to calculate the current population of this imaginary country.

Population one year ago	1000
Birth rate	15 per 1000
Death rate	10 per 1000
Number of immigrants in the year	8
Number of emigrants in the year	5

2 Movement in the city

Figure 1 Information about Northampton

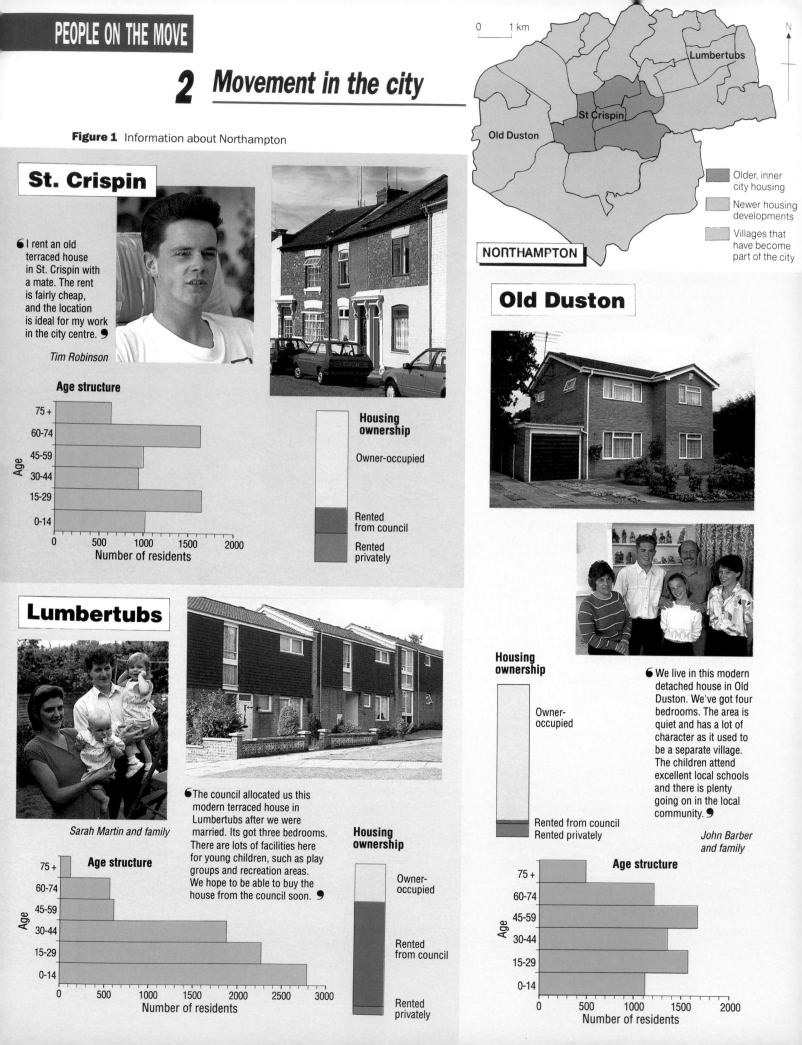

St. Crispin

❝I rent an old terraced house in St. Crispin with a mate. The rent is fairly cheap, and the location is ideal for my work in the city centre.❞

Tim Robinson

Age structure

Number of residents

Housing ownership

Owner-occupied

Rented from council

Rented privately

Old Duston

Housing ownership

Owner-occupied

Rented from council
Rented privately

❝We live in this modern detached house in Old Duston. We've got four bedrooms. The area is quiet and has a lot of character as it used to be a separate village. The children attend excellent local schools and there is plenty going on in the local community.❞

John Barber and family

Age structure

Number of residents

Lumbertubs

Sarah Martin and family

❝The council allocated us this modern terraced house in Lumbertubs after we were married. Its got three bedrooms. There are lots of facilities here for young children, such as play groups and recreation areas. We hope to be able to buy the house from the council soon.❞

Age structure

Number of residents

Housing ownership

Owner-occupied

Rented from council

Rented privately

NORTHAMPTON

0   1 km

N

Lumbertubs

St Crispin

Old Duston

Older, inner city housing

Newer housing developments

Villages that have become part of the city

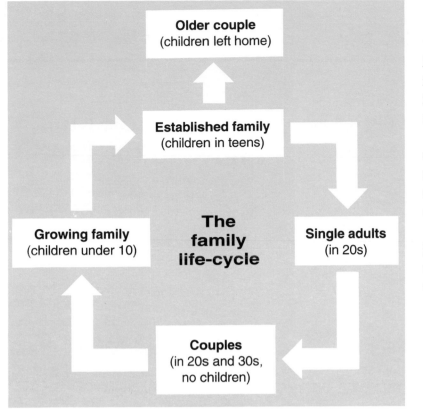

Migration, on a small scale, takes place in cities. People often live all their lives in the same city, but move house when their circumstances change.

Different parts of the city provide suitable housing for people at different stages in the family life-cycle. The diagram in Figure 2 illustrates five key stages in the life-cycle of a family.

By studying the city of Northampton (Figure 1), we can see where families at different stages in the life-cycle choose to live.

Figure 2 The family life-cycle

Activities

1 Study all the information in Figure 1. Copy and complete these statements by filling in the name of the ward (St Crispin, Lumbertubs, or Old Duston).

a) _____ is an inner city ward with nineteenth century terraced housing.

b) _____ used to be a separate village, but with the growth of new housing estates it has now merged with the city.

c) _____ is an area of mainly council housing providing homes for families with young children.

d) Nearly 90 per cent of houses in _____ are owned by their occupants.

e) In _____ nearly 20 per cent of all houses are rented privately, often to single people in their twenties.

2 Explain in your own words why Tim Robinson, the Barber family, and the Martin family live where they do.

3 a) Make a list of ten reasons for moving house.
b) For each reason in your list, say whether it is an economic, social, or environmental reason.

4 a) What types of housing would you expect old aged pensioners to live in?
b) Where in Northampton do you think you are likely to find these types of housing?

5 Research idea:
Carry out your own house moving survey in your class. Find out (a) where people have moved from and (b) why people have moved. Present your results using graphs and maps. What conclusions can you make?

3 Moving out

Census figures show that people are moving away from the major cities. The following information illustrates how and why this is taking place.

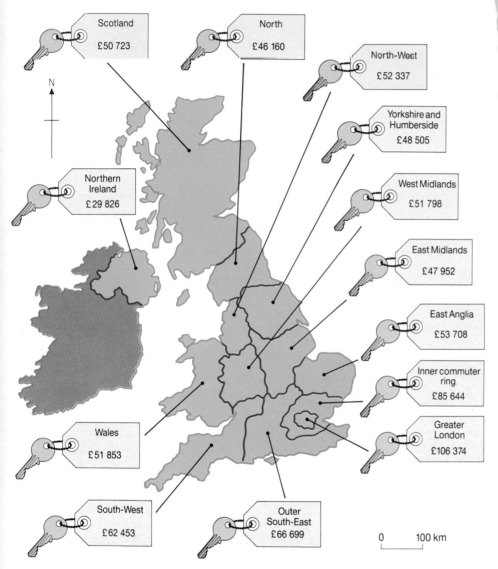

Figure 1 Regional house prices in the UK, 1990. The price shown for each region was the average selling price of a modern three-bedroomed semi-detached house

- Scotland £50 723
- North £46 160
- North-West £52 337
- Yorkshire and Humberside £48 505
- West Midlands £51 798
- East Midlands £47 952
- East Anglia £53 708
- Inner commuter ring £85 644
- Greater London £106 374
- Northern Ireland £29 826
- Wales £51 853
- South-West £62 453
- Outer South-East £66 699

0   100 km

Fed-up Londoners move to the North

Record numbers of companies and employees are being driven out of London by traffic chaos and sky-high mortgages. About 100 firms a week – 25 per cent more than a year ago – are deciding to move to the North of England, Scotland, or Wales.

The attractions are obvious – the average house price in Yorkshire and Humberside is £44,000, less than half that in London and the South-East.

Industrial action on the tube, buses, and railways has increased disillusionment with life in the South-East.

One company which has recently announced plans to go north is Millicom UK, the international telecommunications group. It is moving its European headquarters, employing 200 people, from Battersea, South-West London, to Darlington, County Durham.

Peter Scrope, deputy chairman, said he had been surprised at the number of staff wanting to leave the South-East. 'I think many people realise life is better up there', he said.

Figure 2 Newspaper extract

Figure 3 Newspaper extract

The commuter belt widens

ARE LONDON'S COMMUTERS now willing to put up with longer journeys to work? It seems they are.

Over the last decade more and more Londoners have moved out of the city, looking for cheaper housing and a cleaner, less crowded environment. British Rail has played an important part in this trend.

High-speed trains have cut commuting time down drastically, and electrification will shortly reduce journey times further.

Some local people, however, do not approve of the invasion by commuters. 'They complain that the cows make a mess and church bells wake them on Sunday mornings,' said Mrs. Hart, parish council chairwoman in a Leicestershire village. 'Then they move on, having put house prices up to such an extent that our own children cannot afford to buy a house.'

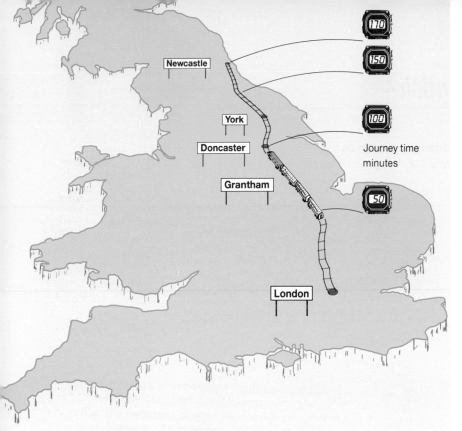

Figure 4 Rail journey times to and from London (main InterCity Eastern Region line)

Journey time minutes

Activities

1 Look at Figure 1.
a) How much more expensive are houses in Greater London than the North of England?
b) Why do you think prices vary so much around the country?

2 Read the newspaper article in Figure 2.
a) Where are some London companies choosing to move to?
b) Give two reasons why these companies are choosing to move.

3 Look at Figures 3 and 4.
a) What is a commuter?
b) How have British Rail encouraged more people to move out of London and commute?
c) What do local people think of the commuters?
d) How long does it take to travel from:
(i) Newcastle to London;
(ii) York to London?

4 Look at Figure 5.
a) Using your atlas, find three counties whose populations had:
(i) increased by more than 8 per cent between 1971 and 1981;
(ii) decreased by more than 5 per cent between 1971 and 1981.
b) Have urban counties or rural counties declined most in population?

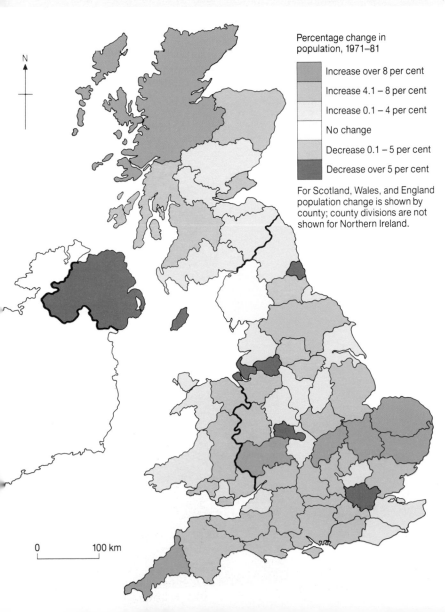

Percentage change in population, 1971–81

Increase over 8 per cent

Increase 4.1 – 8 per cent

Increase 0.1 – 4 per cent

No change

Decrease 0.1 – 5 per cent

Decrease over 5 per cent

For Scotland, Wales, and England population change is shown by county; county divisions are not shown for Northern Ireland.

0   100 km

Figure 5 Map showing population change in the UK, 1971–1981

4 Who are the British?

It is almost impossible to describe a typical British person, because British citizens come from a wide variety of backgrounds.

People have been coming to settle in Britain for thousands of years. Early immigrants were the Celts, Romans, Saxons, and Vikings. More recent immigrants include the Irish, West Indians from the Caribbean, Asians, and other Europeans.

People may make the decision to emigrate to Britain because of the need to escape problems in their native country or because of the opportunities that Britain can offer immigrants.

Let us meet some British citizens from a variety of ethnic backgrounds.

Figure 1 Four British citizens

Hello, I'm Sophie. My mother came here from Italy soon after the Second World War to marry a soldier. She says that things were quite difficult at first, but that they got easier as her English improved. When my father came out of the army they took over a village shop. I've been to Italy to visit our relations.

Hello. My name is Aparna Banerjee. I moved to Britain in 1956 from Calcutta, India, with my husband. We had both worked in the textile trade in India, so we settled here in Leicester where there were lots of jobs in the clothing industry. My husband now runs his own clothing business. We live in an older house near the city centre. There is a large Asian community here. I wear traditional dress, but my three daughters dress in the European way. We are glad we migrated to Britain because opportunities were not available to us in India. We like to keep up Indian traditions, but my children definitely regard themselves as British rather than Indian.

I'm Joe. My great great grandfather was Irish. He moved to England to escape the poverty and starvation in Southern Ireland. Apparently he worked building the Manchester Ship Canal along with many other Irish labourers. He later got a job at the Liverpool Docks, and our family has lived in Liverpool ever since.

Hi, I'm Paul. I was born here. My parents moved to London in 1960 from Jamaica in the Caribbean. They came because of the promise of jobs and housing. My father first worked cleaning out buses at night, then he became a bus driver. We live in a high-rise council flat in Brixton. The flats are in a bad condition and there's a lot of crime in the area.

There are four main groups of immigrants in Britain. There are the Irish, the Europeans, Old Commonwealth immigrants (people from Canada, Australia, and New Zealand), and New Commonwealth immigrants (people from India, Pakistan, Bangladesh, the Caribbean, and certain African countries). Each group has its own reasons for having migrated, and each group tends to settle in different parts of the country.

The most recent migration has been of New Commonwealth citizens, and Figure 2 shows where they originated from. They have emigrated to Britain for a variety of reasons, but one of the most important early factors was Britain's labour shortage after the Second World War. During the war many men had been killed, and so Britain was short of workers to re-build the economy. Britain therefore looked to the New Commonwealth for help.

Country or region of origin	Percentage of New Commonwealth immigrants from each country or region
Caribbean	40%
India	26%
Pakistan/Bangladesh	16%
East Africa (Asians)	11%
Black Africa (Central & West Africa)	7%

Figure 2 Where Britain's New Commonwealth immigrants came from

Figure 3 Why the New Commonwealth immigrants migrated to Britain, and what happened to them

Activities

1 Look at Figure 1. For each of the four people say why they, or their relatives, moved to Britain.

2 What do these terms mean?
a) 'Citizen'
b) 'Ethnic'
c) 'Immigrant'

3 Using the information in Figure 2, draw a flow-line map showing the origins of New Commonwealth immigrants in Britain. The width of the arrow should indicate the percentage of immigrants from that area.

4 Read the cartoon in Figure 3.
a) What does it say about why people migrated to Britain?
b) What point is being made about how some of those people were treated?

5 Research idea:
Carry out your own research to find out about your origins. Have you got any relatives who migrated to Britain from another country? Find out when and why they migrated.

After the Second World War, when Britain wanted workers, it passed the 1948 Nationality Act. This gave Commonwealth citizens rights to come and go ---

Black workers were used to rebuild Britain cheaply and keep its services running ---

They worked in hospitals, factories, and on public transport ---

--- and often got paid less than white workers

The only housing they could get was the run-down inner city areas

Later, people started to say that the black population was the cause of the housing and job shortage ---

The reality was that black people had moved into houses and jobs abandoned by whites

5 Assignment: The multicultural debate

Background information

Surely everyone knows that Britain is now a multicultural society. Of course, it always has been, as you have seen from previous pages. People from different parts of the world have been coming to Britain for centuries, each bringing with them new ideas and customs which have become part of our way of life.

Some of these things are more obvious than others – and certain photos on these pages highlight things that have enriched life in Britain. Other items on these pages pinpoint the less pleasant aspects of a multicultural society.

Your assignment

Your assignment is to think about the following statement, or 'motion', and then to hold a class debate. How you should go about this is outlined in the Work Programme. The motion is:

'This house believes that life in Britain is richer and more varied because of multicultural influences.'

Figure 1 People from different ethnic backgrounds: top sprinter Linford Christie (top), singer-songwriter George Michael (middle), and TV newscaster Lisa Aziz (bottom)

Figure 2 A smiling face amid the colour of Notting Hill Carnival

Figure 3 Chinese food is very popular in Britain

April 12, 1981

THE NIGHT BRIXTON BURNED

HUNDREDS of black youths, joined by some whites, rampaged through Brixton, South London, last night in a violent explosion of anger.

More than 50 police and an unknown number of civilians were injured, some seriously, during several hours of running battles. Dozens of shops were wrecked and burned out by petrol-bombs and there was widespread looting.

Figure 4 Racial tension played a part in the inner city riots of the 1980s

Figure 5 Newspaper headlines about racial harassment

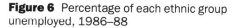

Ethnic group	Per cent unemployed
White	10
Black (West Indian/Guyanese, African)	19
Indian	14
Pakistani/Bangladeshi	27
Other	14

Per cent unemployed

Figure 6 Percentage of each ethnic group unemployed, 1986–88

Work Programme

- Divide into small groups. Each group will be asked to put together arguments either *for* or *against* the motion.
  Remember the purpose of a debate is to give people the chance to hear both sides of an issue. So your job is to focus on your side of the motion, and to argue your case as clearly and fairly as you can.
- In considering the case you are going to argue, try and make use of the following resources:
  (i) the information on these pages;
  (ii) television, newspapers, and magazines;
  (iii) your own experiences and views;
  (iv) other people's experiences and views (you could conduct a survey of pupils in your school, or people in your neighbourhood).
- For the debate, summarise your findings into a short speech that supports the view you are taking. You are now ready to take part in a class debate.

6 Europe's migrants

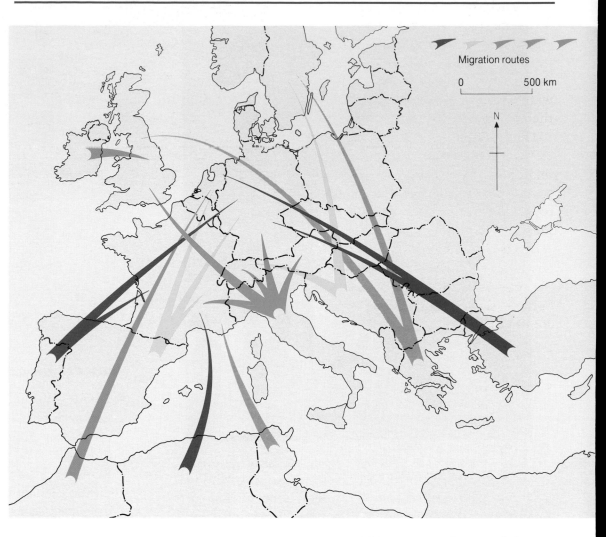

Migration routes

0   500 km

N

Figure 1 This map shows international migration routes in Europe from 1945 until 1991. Most of these movements were for work. Since 1991 there has also been a different type of movement – the break-up of Yugoslavia has caused large numbers of refugees to flee to other countries to escape the fighting

Figure 2 Where West Germany's migrant workers came from

Country	Per cent (%)
Turkey	29
Yugoslavia	17
Italy	15
Greece	7
Spain	4
Portugal	3
France	2
Others	23

During the nineteenth and early twentieth centuries, over 50 million people emigrated from Europe to countries such as the USA, Canada, Australia, and South Africa. The pressure on the resources of Europe, which caused starvation in countries such as Ireland, was one of the main reasons for migration. The invention of the steamship made the journey more possible, and as people settled in the 'New World' more and more Europeans heard of the opportunities and decided to migrate.

The twentieth century has seen a reversal of this trend, with many people, often from developing countries, deciding to migrate to Europe. Within Europe, the search for work has been the major cause of migration since 1945. The map in Figure 1 illustrates some of the important international migrations.

Before reunification in 1990, West Germany had been one of the major recipients of migrant workers in Europe. The urgent need for workers in the late 1950s saw the start of the migration to West Germany.

By the 1980s, there were 4.5 million migrant workers in the country, forming 7.4 per cent of the population.

Turks form the largest group of migrant workers in Germany. They wanted to escape the low standard of living and shortage of jobs at home.

At first they worked in farming, but they soon picked up the factory jobs the German workers did not want. The jobs were unskilled, poorly paid, and demanded long working hours.

The population pyramid in Figure 4 illustrates the age-sex distribution of the Turkish immigrants. Most of them were young men, occasionally bringing their wives and children with them.

The reduced demand for goods in the 1970s and 1980s resulted in many migrant workers losing their jobs. The government introduced a ban on the recruitment of foreign workers after 1973, and in 1980 new laws encouraged Turks to return home. Most stayed, however, and cities such as Berlin, Cologne, Frankfurt, and Dusseldorf have developed large Turkish communities.

PEOPLE ON THE MOVE

Figure 3 Turkish migrant workers in one of Germany's car factories

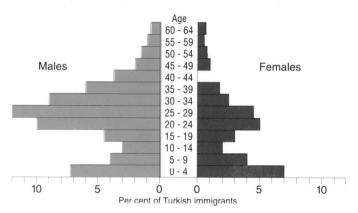

Figure 4 (right) The population pyramid for Turkish immigrants in Germany

Activities

1 a) Where did Europeans emigrate during the nineteenth and early twentieth centuries?
   b) Why did the Europeans emigrate?
2 Look at the map in Figure 1. Using the map on page 94 to help you, answer the following questions.
   a) Name the five countries Italian's emigrated to.
   b) Where did West Germany's immigrants come from?
   c) Name all the countries that:
   (i) received migrants;
   (ii) sent migrants.
   d) How are the 'receiving' countries different from the 'sending' countries?
3 Using the information in Figure 2, draw a pie chart to show the origin of migrant workers in West Germany.

4 Look at Figure 4.
   a) Which age group has the largest percentage of male immigrants?
   b) Why is there such a large percentage of immigrants in the 20–39 age category?
   c) Why are there fewer female immigrants?
5 Copy and complete the table below by thinking of other advantages and disadvantages of migration to the countries involved.

	Advantages	**Disadvantages**
Turkey	1 Reduces the number of unemployed people 2	1 Loses people in the working age group 2
Germany	1 Solves the problem of a labour shortage 2	1 Racial tension 2

71

7 Brazil's population

Figure 1 A crowd of Brazilians. Brazil is a multi-ethnic nation

With a population of 144 million, Brazil is the sixth-largest country in the world in terms of population size.

Most of the people live in the south and east of the country, leaving the Amazon rainforest in the centre and north of the country virtually uninhabited. During the twentieth century, Brazil has experienced a 'population explosion'. This is illustrated in Figure 2. There are two main reasons for this rapid increase in population:

1 The death rate began to fall from about 1940. Improved health care and diet meant people lived longer.
2 The birth rate remained high until the mid-1980s.

Poor health care in the past had resulted in many children dying in the first few years of life, so families were large, often with five or six children. The parents needed their children to help them work on the land and to look after them in old age.

The birth rate, however, began to fall as families moved to the cities and the need for children was not so great. Children in the cities also have more opportunity to attend school, so they are no longer able to help their parents by earning money for the family. The decline in the birth rate has resulted in a slowing down of Brazil's population increase in recent years.

One of the consequences of the population explosion is that a large proportion of Brazil's population is very young, as Figure 3 shows.

Brazil is a multiracial society. The Indians were the original inhabitants, and they have lived in the country in tribal groups for over 3500 years.

The Portuguese were the first immigrants to arrive after 1500. This marked the start of European influence on the country. Brazil became a Portuguese colony and new immigrants claimed land and set up sugar and coffee plantations. They needed cheap labourers, and their solution was to

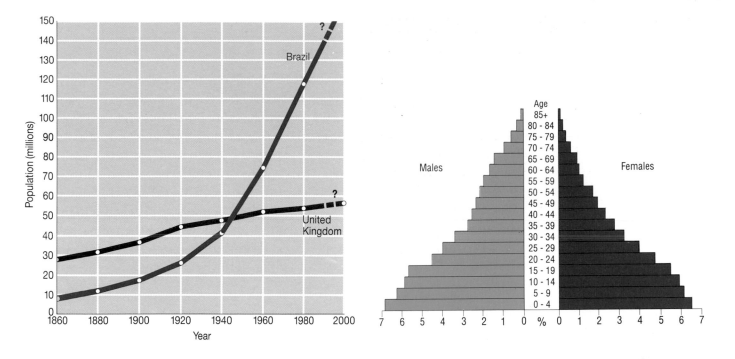

Figure 2 Brazil's population explosion, compared with the population growth of the UK

Figure 3 Brazil's population pyramid, 1981

bring black slaves from West Africa to work on the plantations.

In 1822, Brazil declared itself independent from Portugal. A new phase of immigration brought people from Italy and later Japan and the USA to work on the coffee plantations and set up farms.

Over the centuries, there has been much inter-marriage between the different racial groups. This 'melting pot' has produced a society with harmonious race relations, and given Brazilian people a character of their own.

The biggest differences lie with the Indians, who are now a cause of great concern. Although special reserves have been set aside for the Indians by the government, their culture is still threatened. In 1500 their estimated population was between 2.5 million and 5 million. There are now only 100 000 of them left. Eighty-seven tribes have become extinct through intentional killings by the new settlers, European diseases, or loss of their tribal lands as the Amazon rainforest rapidly disappears.

Activities

1 Look at Figure 2.
a) In which year did Brazil's population become larger than the United Kingdom's?
b) How many years did it take for Brazil's population to double from
(i) 10 to 20 million;
(ii) 20 to 40 million;
(iii) 40 to 80 million?

2 a) What is a 'population explosion'?
b) Why did one occur in Brazil during the twentieth century?
c) What effect has it had on the population pyramid?

3 Using the information on these pages, draw a world map showing from where and when groups of people moved to Brazil.

4 Which population group has been worst affected by the changes in Brazil? Explain why and suggest ways this population group could be helped.

8 The pull of the city

Most people in developing countries live in rural areas, earning a living from farming. However, in recent years, millions of people have chosen to leave the countryside and move to the city, where they believe opportunities are greater.

In 1950, only 30 per cent of the world's population lived in cities. By 1980, 40 per cent were urban dwellers, and by the year 2025 the figure is expected to be over 60 per cent.

Brazil has been one of the countries most affected by rapid urbanisation. Since 1950, Brazil has changed from being a country where 7 out of every 10 people lived in rural areas to a country where 7 out of 10 people now live in urban areas. This urban explosion has resulted in massive cities in which it is difficult to cope with the new arrivals.

Rosa's diary (Figure 1) tells the story of one family's migration to the city.

Figure 1 Rosa's diary

5th June
Manuel, my husband, is again saying we should move to the city. He thinks we can make a better life for ourselves there. I'm still uncertain.

20th June
The harvest looks bad again. Feeding everyone is going to be difficult.

28th June
We heard today that the primary school teacher is leaving, and we don't know when we'll get another. I don't want the children to miss out on an education.

Pedro's home in the city

6th July
Pedro, Manuel's brother, is home from the city for a few days. He left here with his family over a year ago and now works in a car factory. They built their own home in the periferia. They've got electricity and water – it sounds great, better than here! And the children go to school. He says we should go.

12th August
After weeks of discussion, we've finally decided to go.

Manuel and the children

19th August
It didn't take us long to pack our few things. Then we caught the bus for the eight-hour journey to the city. We found Pedro's house and are staying the night. The area is crowded with homes people have built themselves. The open drains make it smelly, but Pedro's house is quite cosy and he says we'll get used to the smell!

20th August
We wanted to live near Pedro, but there's no room. So we walked out towards the edge of the city, into the favelas. People have put up homes everywhere, mostly illegally on land owned by the city authorities. And the further we walked, the more basic the houses became. They're just shacks, built from all sorts of rubbish - timber, old tyres, corrugated iron, plastic sheets, and cardboard. There's no water and no electricity. But at least we've found a space.

Our new home

21st August
We built our new home today, using wood and some cardboard and plastic sheeting Pedro got from the factory. Its only got one room and is very basic, but will do for the moment. We're about 10km from Pedro's and the car factory where Manuel hopes to get a job. I hope we can soon build something better and get water, drainage, and electricity connected. Maybe one day we'll be able to rent somewhere near the city centre. I can't wait!

Figure 2 A cross-section of a typical Brazilian city

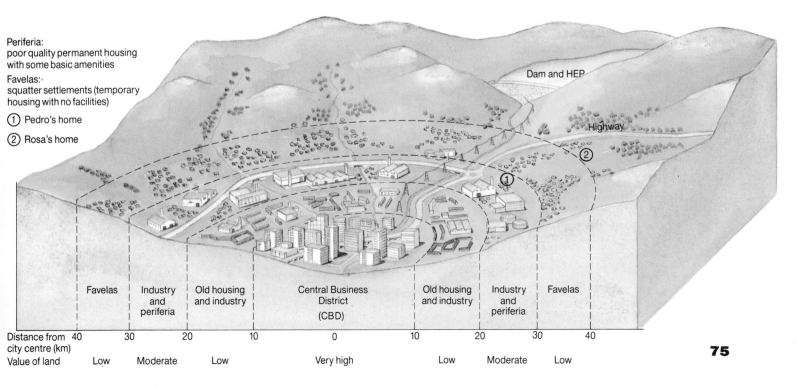

Periferia:
poor quality permanent housing with some basic amenities

Favelas:
squatter settlements (temporary housing with no facilities)

① Pedro's home
② Rosa's home

Dam and HEP

Highway

Favelas	Industry and periferia	Old housing and industry	Central Business District (CBD)	Old housing and industry	Industry and periferia	Favelas

Distance from city centre (km): 40 30 20 10 0 10 20 30 40

Value of land: Low Moderate Low Very high Low Moderate Low

75

The pull of the city

Squatter settlements

Temporary homes built by the poor on land they do not own. Homes lack basic services such as electricity, water, and drainage. Squatter settlements have different names around the world:
Brazil - *favelas*
Peru - *barriadas*
Venezuela - *ranchos*
Chile - *callumpus*
India - *bustees*

Slums

Areas of older housing usually found near city centres. Often run down and overcrowded with poor services

Millionaire cities

Cities with over 1 million inhabitants

Figure 3 Some important terms explained

Country	City	Percentage of city population living in slums and squatter settlements
Argentina	Buenos Aires	20
Brazil	Sao Paulo	40
	Rio de Janeiro	40
	Belo Horizonte	20
	Recife	60
	Brasilia	60
	Porto Alegre	20
Chile	Santiago	40
Colombia	Bogota	60
	Cali	40
Ecuador	Guayaquil	60
Peru	Lima	40
Uruguay	Montevideo	20
Venezuela	Caracas	60
	Maracaibo	60

Figure 4 South America's slum cities

Activities

1 a) Describe the housing in the photographs in Rosa's diary.
b) Choose one of the photographs and draw a sketch of the housing. Label the different materials that have been used to build the house.

2 Read Rosa's diary.
a) Give two reasons why Rosa and Manuel wanted to leave the countryside.
b) What would be the advantages to Rosa and Manuel of moving to the city?
c) How did Rosa and Manuel travel to the city?
d) Describe how the housing changed as Rosa and Manuel walked towards the edge of the city.

3 a) Using the information in Figure 4, and an atlas, plot the millionaire cities onto a map of South America by drawing a small circle at each location. Label the cities.
b) To show the percentage of each city's population living in slums and squatter settlements, use the following colour code to shade in the circle:
41–60 per cent – Black
21–40 per cent – Red
0–20 per cent – Yellow

4 Produce a radio or television programme based on Rosa's experiences of deciding to move to the city. The programme could be a play or a documentary.

Brazilian cities like Sao Paulo and Rio de Janeiro are not the only cities in the world with squatter settlements. Most of the millionaire cities in the developing world have some of their population living in squatter settlements or shanty towns.

Providing decent housing for all their people is perhaps the biggest challenge facing these cities. But there is no easy solution to this problem.

In the assignment on the next page you will be looking at one approach that has been tried in Sao Paulo. Developing countries have, however, adopted several strategies at a variety of scales, as shown in Figure 5.

Self-help housing

- Improved roads, some with street-lighting
- Brieze blocks and cement used
- Separate living and sleeping areas
- Corrugated iron used for roofing
- Bathrooms with showers and toilets
- Water tanks and sinks
- Underground drains
- Electricity connected

Figure 5 What can be done?

Figure 6 Things that might be included in a self-help housing scheme

City authorities can:
- demolish existing squatter settlements and replace them with high-rise flats to be rented by squatter settlement dwellers;
- improve conditions in the squatter settlements by providing services such as electricity, water, and drainage.

WHAT CAN CITY AUTHORITIES DO?

The people who live in squatter settlements can form self-help groups, where they can work together to:
- improve housing conditions;
- provide facilities such as schooling and health care;
- persuade city authorities to provide essential services such as water, electricity, and drainage.

WHAT CAN THE LOCALS DO?

SOLVING THE SQUATTER PROBLEM

WHAT CAN INTERNATIONAL ORGANISATIONS DO?

International organisations, such as the World Bank, can:
- lend money to developing countries for projects to improve services, build new housing, and fund self-help schemes;
- send experts to advise local people and city authorities about possible solutions.

WHAT CAN NATIONAL GOVERNMENTS DO?

National governments can:
- provide money to improve existing housing areas and build new ones;
- persuade people not to move to the cities by providing incentives for them to either stay in the countryside or move to areas that need developing (like the Amazon);
- build new cities (like Brasilia) to attract people away from the older overcrowded cities .

9 Assignment: Solving the squatter problem?

Background information: the proposal

The city authorities in Sao Paulo, Brazil's largest city, have proposed the demolition of one of the favelas. They will build high-rise flats to rent out in place of the self-built homes. The flats will accommodate 1500 people, and will be provided with electricity, water, and drainage. Any other facilities will have to be provided by the flat dwellers.

Background information: the favela

The favela is located approximately 25 kilometres from the centre of Sao Paulo, and is home to 3000 people. It was created about three years ago on a site that was previously used for dumping and is owned by the city authorities. At first there were no services and the homes were very basic. However, a co-operative of favela dwellers was formed, and they have been working to improve the conditions in the area. They managed to persuade the authorities to supply electricity and water to the favela, and they have built a primary school with their own money. There is a very strong community spirit in the favela and the conditions for everyone are slowly being improved.

Background information: the meeting

The city authorities have organised a meeting for everyone who has an interest in the favela to discuss the proposal. The aim of the meeting is to decide whether the scheme should go ahead.

City council representative
Chairperson

- Will the city be more or less attractive when the flats are built?
- Who will be allowed to live in the flats?
- How will the flats be paid for?
- Should favela dwellers not given a flat, be given any compensation?
- How will the building of the flats help unemployment in the city?

Favela occupier

- Who will be allowed to live in the flats?
- What will happen to those not allocated flats?
- Could favela dwellers afford to pay rent?
- Will schools and health care be provided by the authorities?
- Will the community spirit be lost?
- What would it be like to live in a high-rise flat?

Leader of the favela co-operative

- Will all the co-operative's good work be lost?
- Would the money be better spent on improving services in the favela, such as drainage and roads?
- Will all the favela dwellers benefit from the new scheme?
- Will the favela dwellers be given compensation if their homes are demolished?

Figure 1 The six people at the meeting

Schoolteacher in the favela

- Will the school stay open?
- Will all the current pupils be able to attend the school if it stays open?
- Who will pay my salary?
- What will happen to the community spirit?

Wealthy city residents

- Will the flats improve the image of the city?
- Are crime rates likely to increase or decrease because of the flats?
- Could the money be better spent?
- Will people's taxes increase in the city?
- How will wealthy residents benefit from the scheme?

Doctor

- Will the new scheme reduce the amount of disease and poor health in the area?
- Could the money be better spent to help improve the health of more favela dwellers?
- What happens to the favela dwellers while the flats are being built?
- Are the authorities going to set up health care facilities in the area once the flats are built?

Your assignment

Your assignment is to act out this meeting. How you should do this is outlined in the Work Programme.

Work Programme

- Work in groups of six and allocate a role to each person. The roles (Figure 1) are given in the form of a series of questions. Each person will need time before the meeting to consider the likely answers to these questions. You will then be ready to play the part of your character at the meeting.
- Before the start of your meeting, discuss as a group how you are going to make a final decision on the proposal. Answering the following questions might help. Will you have a vote? What happens if the vote is a draw? Do some people at the meeting have more power than others?
- At the meeting, each member of the group should be given a chance to speak. Once everyone has made a short speech, then the proposal can be discussed openly, and a decision made.
- Everyone in the group should write notes recording the different opinions and any decisions made. After the meeting these should be written up as minutes from the meeting.

79

...he
...port are
... to make
...eaper, and

...d by transport
...argo. Some
meth... ...t are designed to
carry part... ...pes of cargo. For
example, refri...rated lorries are
designed to carry frozen and fresh food.
Other methods of transport are only
suitable for carrying passengers.

Figure 1 A busy container port – this is Southampton

Figure 2 The alternative transport routes, London-Rome

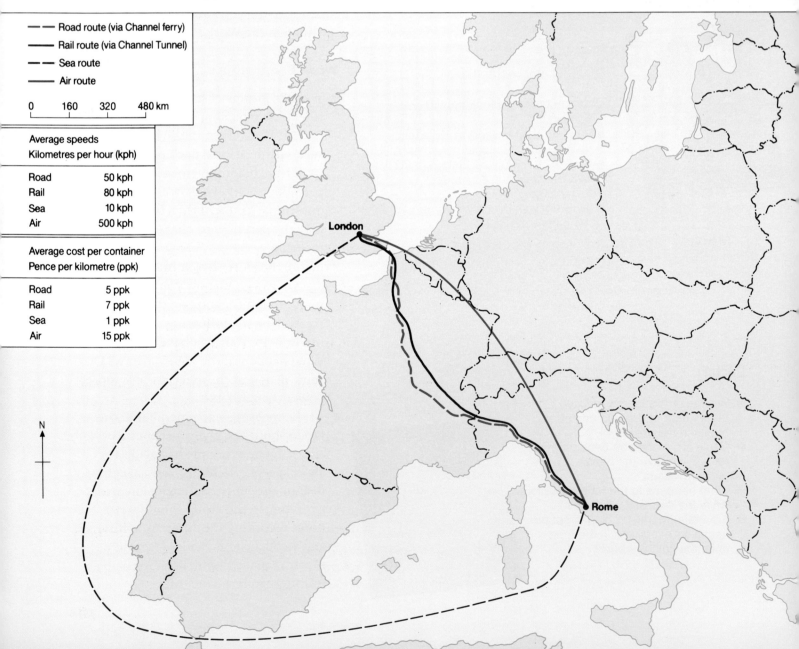

- – – Road route (via Channel ferry)
- —— Rail route (via Channel Tunnel)
- – – Sea route
- —— Air route

0   160   320   480 km

Average speeds Kilometres per hour (kph)	
Road	50 kph
Rail	80 kph
Sea	10 kph
Air	500 kph

Average cost per container Pence per kilometre (ppk)	
Road	5 ppk
Rail	7 ppk
Sea	1 ppk
Air	15 ppk

N

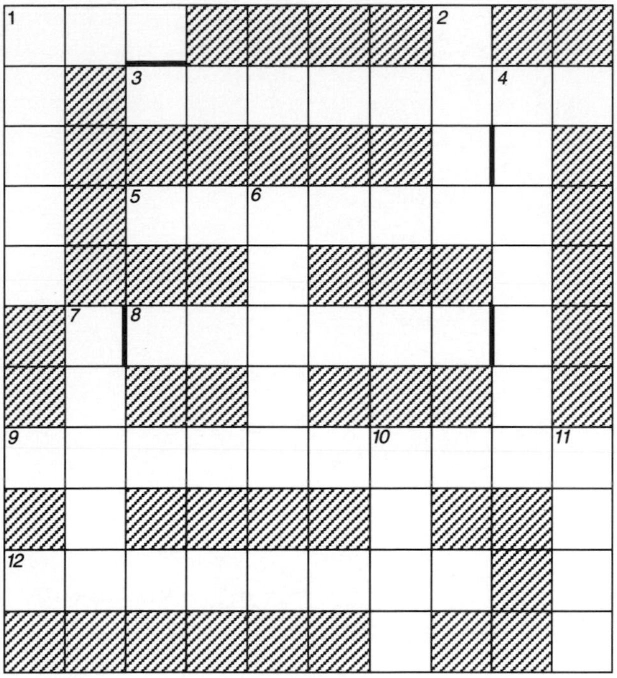

Clues

Across

1 The quickest way to travel (3).
3 Concorde is the fastest of these (8).
5 A two-wheeled vehicle, useful for a paper-round (7).
8 Carries oil around the world (6).
9 A route suitable for horse riders (6,4).
12 The M1, M4, and M6 are all examples of this (8).

Down

1 Carries passengers and cars across the English Channel (5).
2 Carries passengers and cars underneath the English Channel (4).
4 The load of a ship or train (7).
6 Originally transported goods, but now carries holidaymakers in barges (5).
7 Another name for 4 down (5).
10 Baby transport (4).
11 Pay money for short-term use (4).

Figure 3 Transport Crossword

Activities

1 Listed below are some different things which are regularly transported from place to place. What form of transport would normally be used to move them? There may be more than one form for each thing.

Oil   Coal   Mail   People
Furniture   Fresh fruit

2 A problem to solve:
You are the Transport Manager for a computer firm in London. You have just received an order to send a container load of computers to the Banco di Roma in Rome, Italy. You need to decide which is the best way to send the container load of computers.
Look at the map of Europe in Figure 2 showing the four alternative methods of transport and information on average speeds and costs.
a) Copy and complete the following table. Use a piece of string to measure the distances.

Method of transport	Distance (km)	Time of journey (hrs)	Cost (£)
Road Rail Sea Air			

b) What are the advantages and disadvantages of each mode of transport? Consider the number of customs ports to pass, the number of times the container needs to be transferred from one mode of transport to another, security, safety, and so on.
c) Which method of transport do you think would be best to use? Write a short report for your company explaining your decision.
d) If the Banco di Roma are pleased with your computers, they may want to order a lot more. Would you choose the same method of transport for ten container loads of computers? Explain your answer.

3 How much do you know about transport? Test your knowledge by copying and completing the transport crossword in Figure 3.

2 Networks

Britain's motorway system is one of the most important communications networks in the country. A communications network is a pattern of routes (like roads, railways, or telephone lines) connecting a series of points.

When studying a network, it is often useful to change it into its simplest form. The points remain in the same place, but the routes are straightened. This is called a 'topological map'.

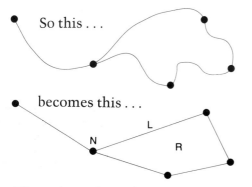

The points where the routes meet are called 'nodes' (N). Lines showing routes are called 'links' (L). Areas enclosed by links are called 'regions' (R).

There are nearly 30 million cars on Britain's roads. Traffic jams are a common problem and it seems that the road network cannot cope with the volume of traffic. One solution is to continue to extend the road network, with the aim of easing congestion and reducing the distance people have to drive to get from one place to another.

The Humber Bridge provides an example of this approach. Until 1981, there was no bridge across the River Humber. This meant that although Kingston-upon-Hull and Scunthorpe are only 29 kilometres apart as the crow flies, the road journey was 84 kilometres. So, a bridge across the Humber was needed to bring the Humberside towns closer together.

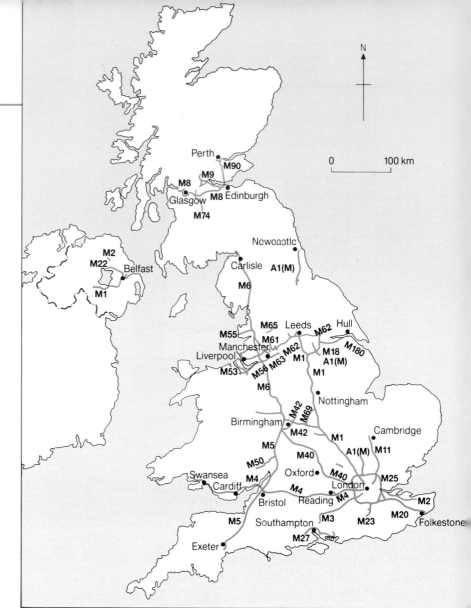

Figure 1 The UK's motorway network

Figure 2 Humberside's road network

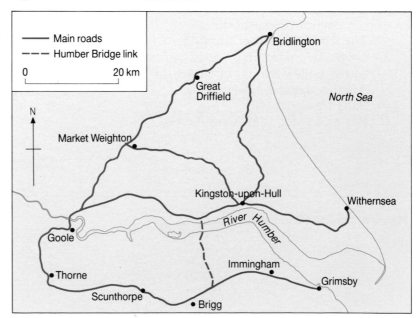

Activities

1 Look at the map of Britain's motorway system in Figure 1.
   a) Which motorway connects London and Leeds?
   b) Which motorway connects Birmingham and Carlisle?
   c) Which two motorways would you use to travel from London to Exeter?
   d) Which city does the M25 circle?
   e) Which parts of Britain have few motorways?
   f) Why do these areas have few motorways?

2 Using the map in Figure 2, draw a topological map of Humberside's road network. Remember to leave out the coastline and river, and draw the roads as straight lines.

3 How did building the bridge improve the road network on Humberside? To answer this question you need to complete an accessibility matrix for the road network before and after the bridge was built. 'Accessibility' means how easy it is to get to a place, and a 'matrix' is a table of numbers.
   a) Make a copy of the accessibility matrix in Figure 3. To fill it in, count the smallest number of links between the nodes, remembering to ignore the Humber Bridge link. For example, the least-links route from Bridlington to Goole takes you through Kingston-upon-Hull and involves two links. Record the number of links in the matrix. The first line has been done for you.
   b) If the most accessible point is the place with the lowest total number

of links, which place was most accessible on Humberside before the bridge was built?
   c) Now draw up another accessibility matrix. Fill it in, this time including the Humber Bridge link.
   d) Which places have gained most from the building of the bridge, and which places have gained least?
   e) What would the following people think about the building of the Humber Bridge? Explain why in each case.
   (i) Lorry driver;
   (ii) Shop owner in Kingston-upon-Hull;
   (iii) Taxpayer in Goole.

Figure 3 The Humber Bridge. It was opened in 1981 and has the longest single central span, 141 metres, of any suspension bridge in the world

Figure 4 Accessibility matrix, before the Humber Bridge link. For use with Activity 3

Number of links	To											Total
From	Br	GD	MW	G	KuH	W	T	Sc	B	I	Gr	
Bridlington (Br)	–	1	2	2	1	2	3	4	5	6	7	33
Great Driffield (GD)		–										
Market Weighton (MW)			–									
Goole (G)				–								
Kingston-upon-Hull (KuH)					–							
Withernsea (W)						–						
Thorne (T)							–					
Scunthorpe (Sc)								–				
Brigg (B)									–			
Immingham (I)										–		
Grimsby (Gr)											–	

3 The M40: the new link

In January 1991, the M40 motorway was completed, forming a direct link between Britain's two largest cities, London and Birmingham. The motorway was needed to improve transport links between the north and the south of the country. The 58-mile stretch of motorway between Oxford and Birmingham cost around £300 million to build, but the cost to the environment is more difficult to measure.

Figure 1 Planning the route of the M40. For use with Activity 1

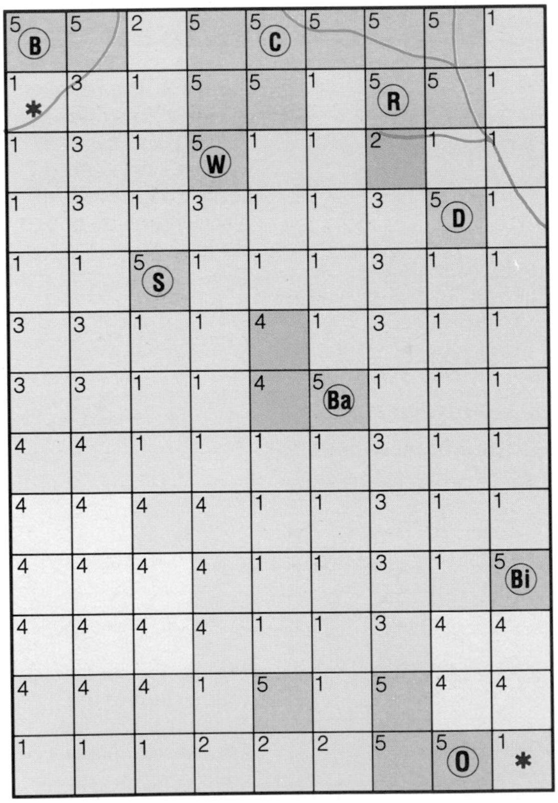

Planning the route of the M40 took a long time and many factors were taken into consideration.

The Department of Transport wanted a direct route that crossed well-drained, flat land. This would have been the least-cost route.

Local people, farmers, and environmentalists were not as concerned about the financial cost, but were worried about the cost to the environment. They preferred a route that by-passed towns and villages, and avoided cutting through areas of natural beauty. They would have liked the least-environmental damage route to have been adopted.

When a Public Inquiry was held in 1982–83 to discuss the proposed M40 route, many interest groups expressed their opinions.

Against the route were:

✗ Nature Conservancy Council
✗ Campaign for the Protection of
✗ Rural England
✗ Transport 2000 (a group in favour of alternative transport systems)
✗ British Butterfly Conservation Society
✗ Campaign to Protect Oxford's Green Belt
✗ The Otmoor Group

For the route were:

✓ M40 Support Group (representatives from industry and local councils)
✓ Port Authorities of Southampton and Portsmouth
✓ Department of Transport

Places

- **B** Birmingham
- **C** Coventry
- **R** Rugby
- **W** Warwick
- **D** Daventry
- **S** Stratford-upon-Avon
- **Ba** Banbury
- **Bi** Bicester
- **O** Oxford

— Existing motorways

✳ Starting and finishing points of the M40

Cost of construction (£ million)

1 Well-drained flat land
2 Area prone to flooding
3 Bridge needed
4 Hills - cuttings and embankments needed
5 Land already built on - high cost to buy and remove existing buildings

Type of environment

- Farmland
- Area of Outstanding Natural Beauty
- Industry and housing
- Recreational use

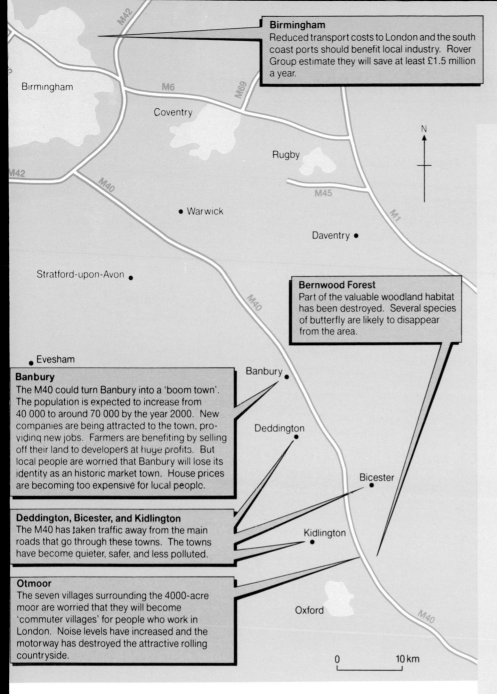

Birmingham
Reduced transport costs to London and the south coast ports should benefit local industry. Rover Group estimate they will save at least £1.5 million a year.

Bernwood Forest
Part of the valuable woodland habitat has been destroyed. Several species of butterfly are likely to disappear from the area.

Banbury
The M40 could turn Banbury into a 'boom town'. The population is expected to increase from 40 000 to around 70 000 by the year 2000. New companies are being attracted to the town, providing new jobs. Farmers are benefiting by selling off their land to developers at huge profits. But local people are worried that Banbury will lose its identity as an historic market town. House prices are becoming too expensive for local people.

Deddington, Bicester, and Kidlington
The M40 has taken traffic away from the main roads that go through these towns. The towns have become quieter, safer, and less polluted.

Otmoor
The seven villages surrounding the 4000-acre moor are worried that they will become 'commuter villages' for people who work in London. Noise levels have increased and the motorway has destroyed the attractive rolling countryside.

0   10 km

Figure 2 The route of the M40

Figure 3 Table for use with Activity 2

Views on the M40

Interest groups	Good points	Bad points
Industrialists		
Conservationists		
Farmers		
Shopkeepers		
Local people		

Activities

1 On tracing paper, make a copy of the grid lines shown in Figure 1. (There is no need to mark on the numbers and colours.)

a) **The least-cost route.**
Place the tracing paper over Figure 1 and work out the least-cost route for the motorway linking up the starting and finishing point symbols. The number in each square indicates how many millions of pounds it would cost to build the motorway across that square. Mark your route onto your tracing paper, and work out how much your route would cost.

b) **The least-environmental damage route.**
Plan a second route trying to avoid areas where the motorway would cause a lot of environmental damage. In particular you need to avoid building in beige squares, and if possible also avoid pink and purple squares. Work out how much this route would cost.

c) Compare your two routes. Is it possible to find a compromise route that would please both groups of people?

2 Copy and complete the table on the left by summarising the views of the various interest groups on the M40.

3 Choose one of the interest groups from the table in Activity 2. *Either* write a letter to a local newspaper expressing the views of the group you have chosen *or* design a poster summarising the views of the group you have chosen.

85

4 Rail: transport of the future or the past?

Mr Loach travels by train from Nottingham to London every weekday. His choice of trains is shown in the timetable in Figure 2, and the route he takes is shown on the InterCity map in Figure 4. However, back in 1980, Mr Loach wrote to the Chairman of British Rail because he was unhappy with the service he was then receiving (Figure 1).

Figure 1 Mr Loach's letter

The Chairman
British Rail

Nottingham
19/12/80

Dear Sir,
I am writing to complain about the poor service you offer.
I commute every weekday from Nottingham to London. Last week, however, the morning train was late twice and cancelled once.
Even when the trains are on time, the journey can be very unpleasant. They are crowded and it is often difficult to get a seat. It is not unusual for the buffet and restaurant service to be unavailable, and British Rail staff can be very unhelpful. It seems that the quality of the service you offer has declined, whilst ticket prices have risen.
I hope the service will soon be improved.

Yours faithfully,

S.E. Loach

S.E. Loach

Sheffield — East Midlands — London 7

There are other non-InterCity trains Bedford — Luton — London.

Mondays to Fridays												
Sheffield			0513		✕			✕		Pg		
Chesterfield			0526						0624	0632	0720	
Derby	0508		0600	0618				0635	0637	0645	0733	
Alfreton & Mansfield									0700		0755	
Nottingham		0537								0656		
Loughborough			0617		0630			0641	0738			0800
Leicester	0530	0600	0630	0645	0647		0705	0718				0817
Market Harborough		0613			0700		0730	0730	0800			0830
Kettering for Corby	0554	0624	0651	0710	0713	0730	0744	0756				
Wellingborough	0601	0631	0658	0719	0724	0739	0804				0851	
Bedford	0614	0644			0732		0828				0859	
Luton	0631	0701s	0722s				0911d					
London St Pancras	0657	0727	0748	0811	0819	0833	0851	0909	0928	0945		

Figure 2 Extract from InterCity timetable

Britain's public railway system began in 1830 with the Liverpool to Manchester Railway. The nineteenth century saw a railway boom, but increased competition from motor vehicles during the twentieth century has seen a gradual decline in the popularity of the railways.

By the 1980s, British Rail was facing a crisis. The railway system was out of date and unreliable. Mr Loach's complaints were typical of many received at the time. As a result, passenger and freight use of the railways declined, as illustrated by Figure 3.

British Rail started to respond to all the criticisms in a variety of ways.

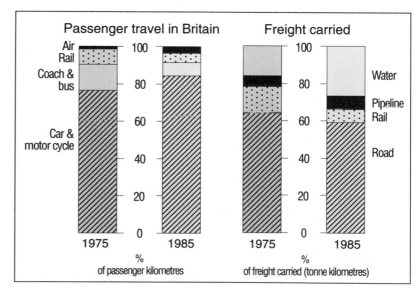

Figure 3 The methods of transport used, 1975 and 1985

New trains have been introduced. InterCity 125s came into operation in 1976. These diesel trains now link the major cities, and travel at speeds of up to 200 kph. Specialised freight trains have been introduced to carry cargoes such as nuclear waste. More electric trains are gradually coming into use as more main lines are electrified. They are capable of speeds up to 224 kph. Work on the Channel Tunnel rail link started in 1987, and this will link Britain with the rest of Europe by the mid-1990s.

British Rail has also made a determined effort to improve the service it offers. A huge advertising campaign was launched to try and improve the image of the railways. All employees were given special training in how to deal with the public, with the aim of improving customer relations. A variety of special rates were introduced to encourage people to use the railways, such as young person's, OAP, and family railcards. Some of the rural railway lines that had been closed during the 1960s were re-opened and computerised signalling was introduced to reduce delays on journeys.

Figure 5 One of British Rail's new trains: the InterCity 225 high-speed electric train

Activities

1 Look at the train timetable in Figure 2.
   a) How long does the 0630 hrs train from Nottingham take to travel to London?
   b) How many stops are there on this route?
   c) Is food available on the 0630 hrs train?

2 Study the InterCity map in Figure 4.
   a) Which station in London would you arrive at if you were travelling from Hull?
   b) Which main towns would you travel through if you were travelling from Norwich to Liverpool Street Station in London?

3 Look carefully at the divided bar graphs in Figure 3. Describe the changes that have taken place in passenger and freight transport between 1975 and 1985.

4 Read Mr Loach's letter and make a list of his complaints.

5 After reading the text about how the railways have been updated, write a letter to Mr Loach from the Chairman of British Rail, informing him of recent developments on the railways. (Assume that the Chairman first replied to Mr Loach in 1980!)

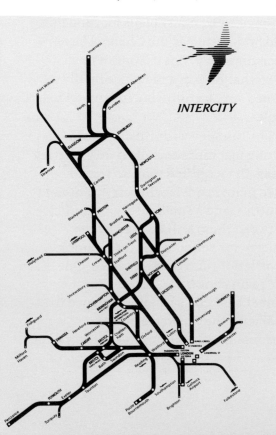

Figure 4 InterCity route map

5 The Channel Tunnel

Britain is no longer an island. On 1st December 1990, when the British and French sections of the Channel Tunnel met up, Britain became linked with France for the first time since the Ice Age, 8000 years ago.

Figure 1

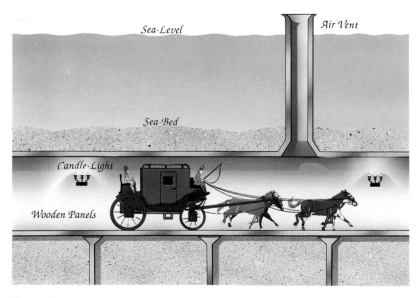

Bonjour! Tunnels join up

Figure 2 Albert Mathieu's proposals for a Channel Tunnel, 1802

Why do we need a tunnel?

1 To increase trade between Britain and Europe.
2 To reduce the danger of a major shipping disaster on the crowded English Channel.
3 To provide a reliable route across the Channel that is not affected by bad weather.
4 To reduce the travelling time between Britain and Europe. Speedier travel should result in less expensive exports and imports. This will result in more British goods being sold in Europe, and cheaper European goods in Britain.

The idea of a fixed link between Britain and France is not a new one. The first proposals were put forward in 1802 when Albert Mathieu, a French engineer, suggested a scheme for two tunnels under the English Channel. Horse-drawn vehicles would have been used for the five-hour journey.

Since 1802, many plans for tunnels and bridges across the Channel have been drawn up. But it was not until 1986 that Britain and France finally signed a treaty allowing the tunnel to be built.

The tunnel was dug using enormous boring machines travelling at 20 metres a day. In fact, three tunnels were dug. Two main tunnels will carry trains and shuttles, and a smaller service tunnel between them will be used by the emergency services and for cleaning, ventilation, and electric cables. One of the main concerns is safety. But the tunnel has been specially designed to deal with the problems of fire, terrorism, suffocation, and the spread of disease by wild or stray animals.

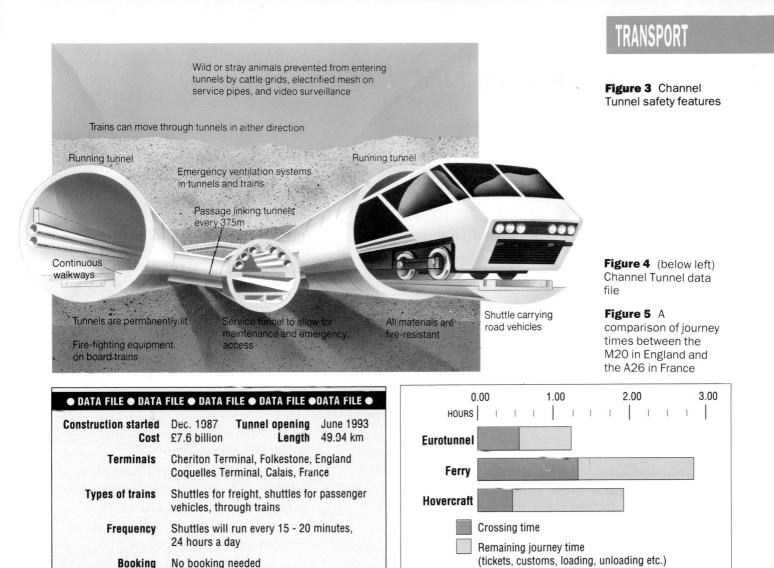

Wild or stray animals prevented from entering tunnels by cattle grids, electrified mesh on service pipes, and video surveillance

Trains can move through tunnels in either direction

Running tunnel

Running tunnel

Emergency ventilation systems in tunnels and trains

Passage linking tunnels every 375m

Continuous walkways

Tunnels are permanently lit

Fire-fighting equipment on board trains

Service tunnel to allow for maintenance and emergency access

All materials are fire-resistant

Shuttle carrying road vehicles

Figure 3 Channel Tunnel safety features

Figure 4 (below left) Channel Tunnel data file

Figure 5 A comparison of journey times between the M20 in England and the A26 in France

● DATA FILE ● DATA FILE ● DATA FILE ● DATA FILE ●DATA FILE ●

Construction started	Dec. 1987	**Tunnel opening**	June 1993
Cost	£7.6 billion	**Length**	49.04 km
Terminals	Cheriton Terminal, Folkestone, England Coquelles Terminal, Calais, France		
Types of trains	Shuttles for freight, shuttles for passenger vehicles, through trains		
Frequency	Shuttles will run every 15 - 20 minutes, 24 hours a day		
Booking	No booking needed		

HOURS   0.00   1.00   2.00   3.00

Eurotunnel

Ferry

Hovercraft

■ Crossing time

□ Remaining journey time (tickets, customs, loading, unloading etc.)

Activities

1 Copy and complete the following paragraph.

Work on the Channel Tunnel began in _____ _____, and it will take _____ years and _____ months to construct. There are _____ tunnels in total, with the central one acting as a _____ tunnel. Passengers arriving in cars at the British terminal in _____ will drive onto the _____ trains. These will run every 15–20 minutes, _____ hours a day.

2 Write a short newspaper report to go with the photograph in Figure 1.

3 Look at Figure 5. How much quicker is the total journey time by Eurotunnel than by (a) ferry (b) hovercraft?

4 Study Mathieu's plans for a Channel Tunnel (Figure 2). List three problems that he would have had with the tunnel if he had tried to build it.

5 Produce a brochure or poster advertising the Channel Tunnel to the British public. Make sure you stress all the advantages the Channel Tunnel has over other methods of crossing the Channel. You will also need to stress the safety features of the tunnel.

6 Assignment: The Channel Tunnel enquiry

Figure 1 What the farmers say

High speed TGV train lines have been built across my land. I don't complain because it's the future. Nobody is against the tunnel link because it will benefit our whole area. We were puzzled when we heard that the British were protesting against the railway. We are proud of it because it is a symbol of France. It is a question of patriotism.

Raymond Decleny
farmer from North-East France

British Rail's proposed high-speed rail link runs across my land. They have offered me compensation, but what price can you put on ruining my livelihood? The rail link will destroy this part of Kent, carving up the landscape, demolishing houses and causing significant noise pollution. We just want to be left alone.

Bob Gagg
farmer from North Kent, England

Background information

Do you love it, or loathe it? The public's response to the construction of the Channel Tunnel and the high-speed rail link from Paris to London has varied enormously. Figure 1 outlines the opinions of many of the French and British farmers affected by the rail link.

Wherever you live in Britain, the Channel Tunnel is likely to have an important impact on your community. But people in your community may have very different views on the tunnel.

Your assignment

Your assignment is to conduct a geographical enquiry into what people in your area think of the Channel Tunnel, and what effects the tunnel might have on your local area. How you should go about this is outlined in the Work Programme.

Figure 2 The Channel Tunnel under construction

Work Programme

The enquiry process
Geographers have a certain way of conducting an enquiry. For your assignment on the Channel Tunnel you need to follow these stages:

STAGE 1

The purpose of the enquiry

You need to answer these questions:
1 What is the aim of your enquiry?
2 What important questions are you trying to investigate?

You may want to set up a hypothesis which states what you expect to find out.

Example The Channel Tunnel enquiry

Aims
1 To find out what local people think about the Channel Tunnel.
2 To find out what effect the Channel Tunnel is likely to have on the local area.

Key questions
What do local people know about the Channel Tunnel?

Are local people in favour of the Channel Tunnel?

What are people's concerns about the tunnel?

What benefits will the tunnel bring for local people?

Are local people likely to use the tunnel?

What effect will the tunnel have on local industry?

Hypothesis
The Channel Tunnel will have a positive effect on the local community.

STAGE 2 Data collection

How are you going to collect the information needed to help you answer the key questions you have asked?

One method is to use a questionnaire. When using questionnaires, it is important to think about the type of questions you are asking.

'Closed questions' provide good statistics on which to base graphs.
Example How often do you expect to use the Channel Tunnel?
❏ never   ❏ once or twice a year
❏ less than once a year   ❏ more than twice a year
Tick as appropriate.

'Open questions' provide a wide range of answers, but it is difficult to present the information.
Example What are your views on the Channel Tunnel?

It is also important to think about your sample. Is it of a reasonable size? (Say between 10 and 50 people.) Have you asked a good range of people in terms of age, sex, jobs, and where they live?

STAGE 3 Presenting the data

Information and data collected can be displayed in a variety of different ways. You need to explain why a particular method of data presentation was chosen.

Examples Bar graphs   Maps   Tables of figures   Diagrams
            Line graphs   Pie charts Sketches   Pictograms
            Photographs   Statistics (e.g.mean, mode,median)

Use at least two different methods to display the information you have collected.

STAGE 4 Interpretation and analysis

Describe the patterns shown on your graphs and maps and so on.
What do these patterns tell you?

STAGE 5 Conclusions

Answer the questions you set yourself in Stage 1. Is your hypothesis correct? Can you explain the results?

STAGE 6 Evaluation

How successful was your enquiry?
What could have been done to improve your research and presentation?
What are the implications of your findings?

7 The transport debate

What is the future of transport in Britain? Are we looking at longer traffic jams, more air pollution, and increased petrol prices, or are there some solutions to Britain's transport problems?

Figure 1 illustrates some of the problems created by different methods of transport, and Figure 3 suggests some of the possible solutions.

Other countries have already adopted some of these ideas. In Brazil, alcohol is made from sugar cane and used successfully in motor vehicles as a fuel. In Australia, many different solar-powered vehicles have been developed. In France, the government has provided money to improve the railway network. The country now has a fast and efficient rail service based on electric trains.

Figure 1 Transport problems

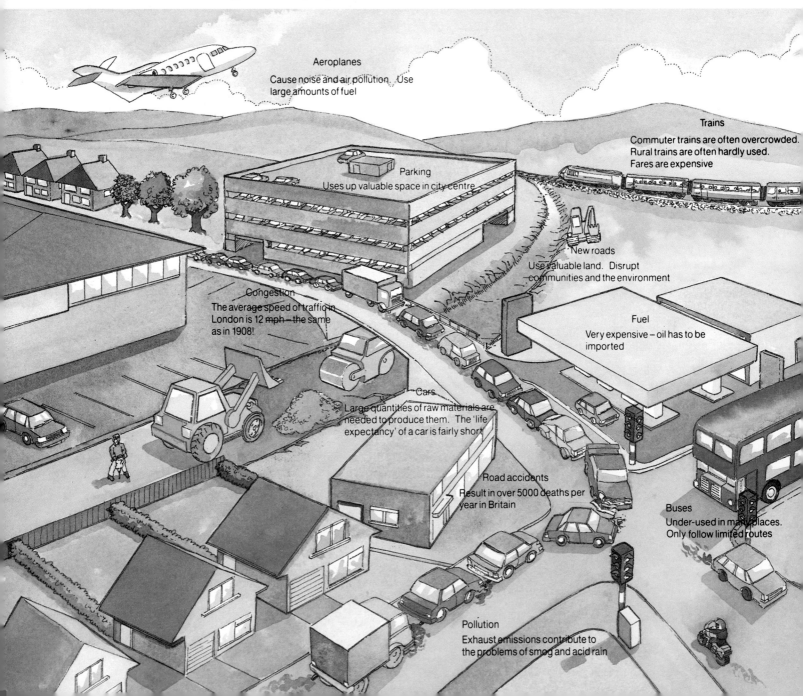

Aeroplanes
Cause noise and air pollution. Use large amounts of fuel

Trains
Commuter trains are often overcrowded. Rural trains are often hardly used. Fares are expensive

Parking
Uses up valuable space in city centre

New roads
Use valuable land. Disrupt communities and the environment

Congestion
The average speed of traffic in London is 12 mph – the same as in 1908!

Fuel
Very expensive – oil has to be imported

Cars
Large quantities of raw materials are needed to produce them. The 'life expectancy' of a car is fairly short

Road accidents
Result in over 5000 deaths per year in Britain

Buses
Under-used in many places. Only follow limited routes

Pollution
Exhaust emissions contribute to the problems of smog and acid rain

TRANSPORT QUESTIONNAIRE

Figure 2

1 How do you travel to school?
a car
b public transport
c bicycle
d walk

2 How many motor vehicles does your family own?
a three or more
b two
c one
d none

3 What type of fuel does your motor vehicle use?
a four-star petrol
b diesel
c lead-free petrol
d none (no car)

4 How many airflights have you been on in your life?
a five or more
b three or four
c one or two
d none

5 Which of the following statements do you most agree with?
a I would never travel on public transport
b Public transport is fine for people who cannot drive, but a waste of time for those who can
c People should be encouraged to travel to work on public transport
d The number of cars and lorries in Britain should be reduced drastically

Activities

1 Find out if you are a 'Transport Troublemaker' by completing the questionnaire in Figure 2.

Scoring

The points for each answer are as follows:
a 4pts   b 3pts   c 2pts   d 1pt

Work out your total score.

If you scored **under 7**: Excellent!
You are definitely not a transport troublemaker.

If you scored **8 - 15**: Not bad. You are causing some environmental damage through your use of transport, but you are aware of the problems.

If you scored **16 - 20**: Oh dear!
You are a definitely a transport troublemaker.

2 Look at the diagram illustrating transport problems in Figure 1. Decide whether each problem is an environmental, social, or economic one, and list it in a copy of the table below. Some problems may be in more than one column.

ENVIRONMENTAL PROBLEM (damages the environment)	SOCIAL PROBLEM (harms people and communities)	ECONOMIC PROBLEM (costs money and damages resources)
Pollution		

3 Read the suggested solutions in Figure 3.
Which solution do you (a) most agree with and (b) least agree with? Explain your answers.

4 Working in small groups, discuss your ideas for solving Britain's transport problems. Produce a group report outlining your suggestions that could be presented to the government. You may want to include maps and diagrams in your report.

Car tax and fuel costs should be increased to put people off using their cars.

Money should be spent on developing alternative forms of fuel for motor vehicles, such as solar power and electricity.

The government should spend more money on public transport. Rail and bus fares should be reduced and the service improved.

The government should spend more money on building new roads and widening existing roads.

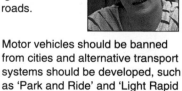

Motor vehicles should be banned from cities and alternative transport systems should be developed, such as 'Park and Ride' and 'Light Rapid Transit'.

Figure 3 Possible solutions to Britain's transport problems – suggestions from five people

— international boundary

• capital city

abbreviations:
AUST.	AUSTRIA
B	BOSNIA-HERZEGOVINA
BELG.	BELGIUM
C	CROATIA
CENT. AF. REP.	CENTRAL AFRICAN REPUBLIC
CZECH.	CZECHOSLOVAKIA
L	LIECHTENSTEIN
LUX.	LUXEMBOURG
NETH.	NETHERLANDS
S	SLOVENIA
SWITZ.	SWITZERLAND
U.A.E.	UNITED ARAB EMIRATES
U.S.A.	UNITED STATES OF AMERICA

Modified Gall Projection

GREENLAND
(Den.)

•Godthåb
(Nuuk)

Alaska
(USA)

C A N A D A

U. S. A.

•Washington
D.C.

Azores
(Port.)

Bermuda
(U.K.)

Hawaiian Is.
(USA)

Nassau
THE
BAHAMAS

Havana• •CUBA

M E X I C O

México•

GUATEMALA
Guatemala•
San Salvador•
EL SALVADOR

•Belmopan
BELIZE

•HONDURAS
Tegucigalpa
•NICARAGUA
Managua•
•San José
COSTA RICA Panamá•
PANAMA

JAMAICA HAITI
Kingston•

DOMINICAN
REPUBLIC
Puerto
Rico
(U.S.A.)

ST. KITTS-NEVIS

•DOMINICA

ST. LUCIA•
ST. VINCENT• •BARBADOS
•GRENADA
TRINIDAD AND
TOBAGO

CAPE VERDE IS.•

Caracas•
VENEZUELA
•Georgetown Paramaribo

GUYANA

•Cayenne
SURINAM FRENCH GUIANA

Bogotá•
COLOMBIA

Galapagos
Is. (Ec.)

Quito•
ECUADOR

P E R U

B R A Z I L

Lima•

•La Paz
BOLIVIA

Brasília•

PARAGUAY

•Asunción

C H I L E

A R G E N T I N A

Santiago•

URUGUAY

Buenos•
Aires •Montevideo

Falkland Is. (U.K.)
•Stanley

South Georgia
(U.K.)

Antarctica
A world map like this cannot show
Antarctica accurately.
Antarctica requires a separate map.

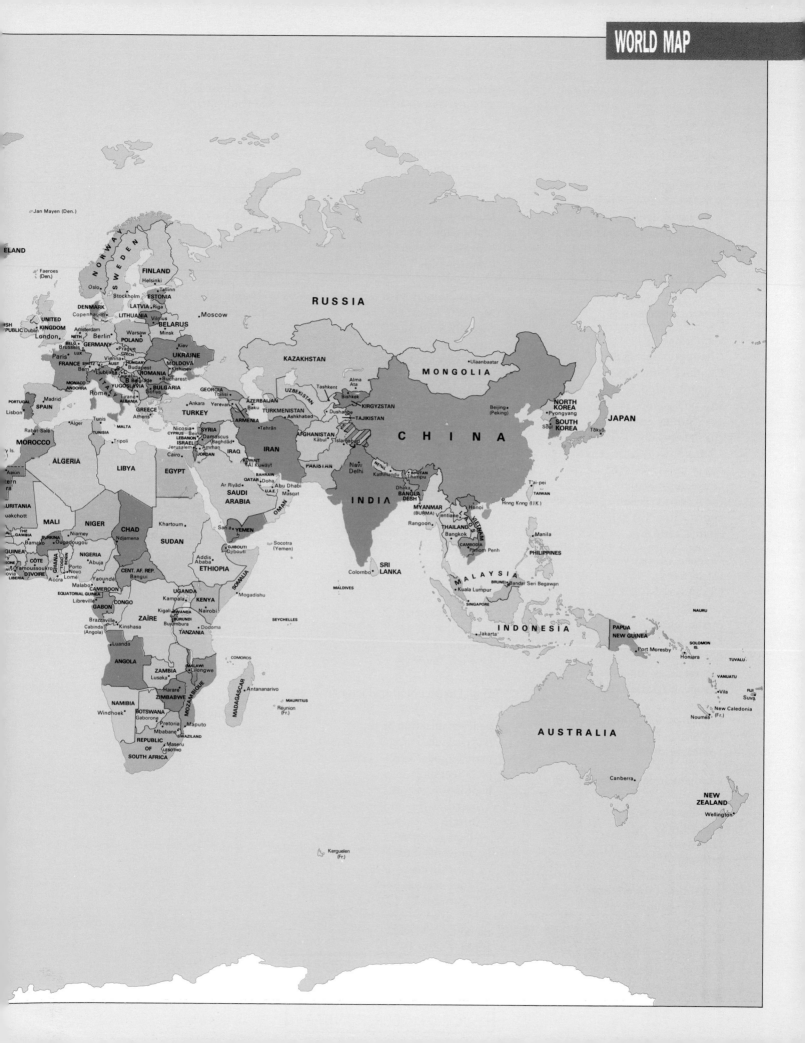

ELAND

Jan Mayen (Den.)

Faeroes
(Den.)

ISH
PUBLIC Dublin
London

NORWAY
SWEDEN
Oslo
Stockholm

FINLAND
Helsinki

DENMARK
Copenhagen

LATVIA Riga
LITHUANIA Vilnius

ESTONIA
Tallinn

Moscow

RUSSIA

UNITED
KINGDOM
Amsterdam
NETH.
BELG.
Brussels
Paris
FRANCE SWITZ.
Bern
MONACO
ANDORRA
PORTUGAL
Lisbon
SPAIN
Madrid

Berlin
GERMANY
LUX.
Prague
CZECH
Vienna
AUST.
Ljubljana

Warsaw
POLAND

Minsk
BELARUS

Kiev
UKRAINE

MOLDOVA
Kishinev

KAZAKHSTAN

Ulaanbaatar

MONGOLIA

HUNGARY
Budapest
ROMANIA
Bucharest
BULGARIA
Sofiya
ITALY
Rome
YUGOSLAVIA
Tirane
ALBANIA

GEORGIA
Tbilisi
ARMENIA
Yerevan

AZERBAIJAN
Baku

UZBEKISTAN
Tashkent

Alma
Ata

Bishkek
KIRGYZSTAN

Beijing
(Peking)

NORTH
KOREA
Pyongyang

JAPAN

GREECE
Athens
TURKEY
Ankara

TURKMENISTAN
Ashkhabad

Dushanbe
TAJIKISTAN

SOUTH
KOREA
Soul

Tōkyō

Rabat-Salé
MOROCCO
Alger
TUNISIA
Tunis
MALTA
Tripoli

Nicosia
CYPRUS
LEBANON
ISRAEL
Jerusalem
SYRIA
Damascus
Baghdâd
JORDAN
Amman
IRAQ

AFGHANISTAN
Kābul
Islamabad

CHINA

T'ai-pei

TAIWAN

ls.

y Is.

ALGERIA

LIBYA

EGYPT
Cairo

KUWAIT
Al Kuwāyt
BAHRAIN
QATAR Doha
Ar Riyād Abu Dhabi
U.A.E.
Masqat

IRAN
Tehrān

PAKISTAN

New
Delhi
Kathmandu
NEPAL
BHUTAN
Thimpu

Dhaka
BANGLA-
DESH

Hong Kong (U.K.)

Aaiun
ern
ra

URITANIA
uakchott

MALI

NIGER

Khartoum

SAUDI
ARABIA

OMAN

INDIA

MYANMAR
(BURMA)
Rangoon

Hanoi
Vientiane
LAOS
VIETNAM

THE
GAMBIA
Bamako
GUINEA
SIERRE
ovia
LIBERIA
CÔTE
D'IVOIRE
Yamoussoukro
Accra

BURKINA
Niamey
Ouagadougou
BENIN
GHANA
TOGO
Porto
Novo
Lomé

CHAD
Ndjamena

NIGERIA
Abuja

San'a
YEMEN

DJIBOUTI
Djibouti

Addis
Ababa
ETHIOPIA

SOMALIA

Socotra
(Yemen)

THAILAND
Bangkok
CAMBODIA
Phnom Penh

Manila

PHILIPPINES

SUDAN

MALDIVES

SRI
LANKA
Colombo

MALAYSIA
Kuala Lumpur
BRUNEI
Bandar Seri Begawan

SINGAPORE

NAURU

GUINEA
BISSAU

CENT. AF. REP.
Bangui
CAMEROON
Yaounde
Malabo
EQUATORIAL GUINEA
Libreville
GABON
CONGO
Brazzaville
Kinshasa
Cabinda
(Angola)
ZAÏRE

UGANDA
Kampala
Kigali
RWANDA
BURUNDI
Bujumbura

KENYA
Nairobi

Dodoma
TANZANIA

Mogadishu

SEYCHELLES

Jakarta

INDONESIA

PAPUA
NEW GUINEA

Port Moresby

SOLOMON
IS.
Honiara

TUVALU

Luanda

COMOROS

ANGOLA
ZAMBIA
Lusaka

MALAWI
Lilongwe
Harare
ZIMBABWE

MADAGASCAR
Antananarivo

MAURITIUS

Réunion
(Fr.)

VANUATU
Vila
FIJI
Suva

New Caledonia
Noumea (Fr.)

NAMIBIA
Windhoek
BOTSWANA
Gaborone
Pretoria
Maputo
MOZAMBIQUE

AUSTRALIA

REPUBLIC
OF
SOUTH AFRICA
Mbabane
SWAZILAND
Maseru
LESOTHO

Canberra

NEW
ZEALAND
Wellington

Kerguelen
(Fr.)